Analogue Electronics for Higher Studies

002

Other Macmillan titles for engineers

Analogue Electronics
for Higher Studies

B. W. Allen
Lecturer in Electronics
Loughborough College

MACMILLAN

First published 1995 by
MACMILLAN PRESS LTD
Houndmills, Basingstoke, Hampshire RG21 2XS
and London
Companies and representatives
throughout the world

ISBN 0–333–60683–3

A catalogue record for this book is available
from the British Library.

10   9   8   7   6   5   4   3   2   1
04   03   02   01   00   99   98   97   96   95

Printed and bound in Great Britain by
Antony Rowe Ltd
Chippenham, Wiltshire

Contents

Preface

This book has not been written because I think I know more about Analogue Electronics than most, nor because the information contained in it is unavailable elsewhere. It has been produced because I felt that many books currently available did not present the relevant material in the best and easiest-to-follow manner. Therefore, throughout the book, whether deriving a mathematical expression, introducing a new concept or simply making a reference to a diagram I have tried to put myself in the student's position of having to extract as much information as possible with as little effort as possible.

I have endeavoured to take the student from lower levels of study to the higher level content with as little pain as possible, often repeating some area of Electronics or Electrical Principles in order to establish the required knowledge base. I have worked through the mathematics of subject areas in a logical and detailed manner, often explaining the mathematical process that is being employed. I have tried to eliminate the need for the reader to flip over pages to link an explanation with its associated diagram, an annoying problem encountered many times personally. In addition I have included a comprehensive index that should allow the reader to locate a reference to a term or topic area.

I have included many 'notes' in order to remind the reader of basic, but vital, information. Some of these may appear simple and obvious but many years of lecturing in this subject area have taught me not to take things for granted, or to assume that all students understand, or can remember, everything that they studied in earlier years.

Some up-to-date data sheets have been included in the book to illustrate how the latest developments have affected device specifications. By employing new and varied technologies, companies such as Texas Instruments, Philips Semiconductors and Maxim Integrated Products are producing linear devices with specifications well beyond those of three or four years ago.

I would like to take this opportunity to thank some people and organisations for their assistance with various aspects of the production of this book.

For their help in providing up-to-date information on current commercial devices I would like to thank

- Claire Garner of Philips Semiconductors Ltd
- Ken Bloom of Maxim Integrated Products (U.K.) Ltd
- David Slatter and others at Texas Instruments Ltd

I would also like to thank

- Adrian Espin of Number One Systems Ltd and
- CRaG Systems

for evaluation copies of 'Analyser III' and 'TopSpice' electronic circuit analysis software.

I would like to thank my colleagues in the Electronics Division at Loughborough College

- Alan Shaw
- Mike Limb and
- Ken Minsky

for their support and assistance in my early years as a lecturer of Analogue Electronics.

Most of all, however, I would like to express enormous thanks to my wife, Debra, for her immense support, encouragement and assistance over the many months taken to complete this book.

1 Small Signal Amplifiers

In this chapter the small signal amplifier will be considered. Transistor circuits will be used, predominantly in common-emitter configuration. Initially lower level work will be covered in order to establish a suitable threshold from which to start the high level work. From that point the small signal amplifier will be analysed, the end products being an understanding of the h parameter equivalent circuit and the derivation of the expression for amplifier voltage gain.

1.1 The transistor amplifier

The circuit diagram of a small signal transistor amplifier is as indicated in figure 1.1.

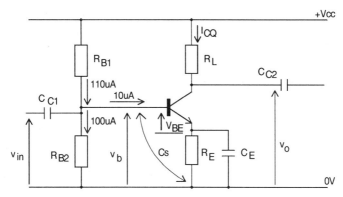

Figure 1.1 *The common emitter amplifier*

1

The circuit will be analysed under d.c. and a.c. conditions in order to determine some typical values for voltage and current around the circuit.

1.1.1 Typical circuit values

Components

R_{B1}: 80 kΩ	R_{B2}: 10 kΩ	R_L: 5 kΩ	R_E: 1 kΩ
C_E: 100 μF	C_C: 10 μF	C_s: 100-900 pF	

DC Parameters

V_{cc}: 10 V	V_o (V_{cq}): 5 V	V_b: 1.65 V	V_e: 1.0 V
V_{be}: 0.65V	I_b: 10 μA	I_{cq}: 1 mA	h_{fe}: 100

Note: When considering the values of biasing components the following points should be borne in mind:

- ☐ **the bleed current through R_{B1} and R_{B2} should exceed I_{Bmin} by a factor >10 (i.e. a minimum of 100 μA).**
- ☐ **X_{CE} should be approximately 0.1 × R_E at the lowest frequency of operation of the amplifier.**

Consideration of the a.c. signals around the amplifier is best achieved with the aid of waveforms. The following sequence of illustrations, figures 1.2 through 1.6, traces a sine wave from the input to the output indicating possible values for both the d.c. biasing levels and a.c. signals.

Note that the only change in phase of the signal occurs when the output current is developed across the output load resistor.

This takes place because the load resistor is connected between the collector of the transistor and the positive supply rail. As the current through the load resistor increases, so the voltage dropped across it increases. However, an increase in voltage dropped across R_L causes the collector voltage to fall, producing an inversion of the signal between base (input) and collector (output).

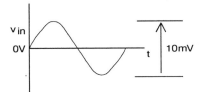

Figure 1.2 *Input voltage*

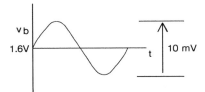

Figure 1.3 *Base voltage*

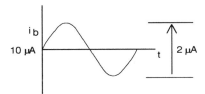

Figure 1.4 *Base current*

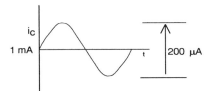

Figure 1.5 *Collector current*

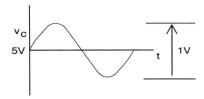

Figure 1.6 *Collector voltage*

1.1.2 Circuit modelling

In order to analyse the performance of a transistor amplifier it is necessary to have an equivalent circuit or 'model' of the active component, i.e. the transistor. Many different models have been used for analysis over the years, including impedance (Z), admittance (Y) and conductance (G), usually with circuit elements arranged in a T circuit. However, this book will employ a combination of these called a hybrid or h parameter equivalent circuit. h parameters have been selected because the equivalent circuits are simpler than many of those mentioned and because manufacturers' data is readily available.

As with all of the models mentioned, the transistor is considered to be a 2-port or 4-terminal network. Irrespective of the contents of the network, only two electrical quantities are measurable at its input and output, namely voltage and current.

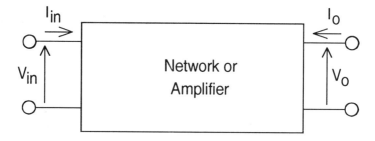

Figure 1.7 *Two-port network*

1.2 h parameters

In general, four parameters are derived from a network such as that shown in figure 1.7. These are usually termed

- □   input parameter
- □   output parameter
- □   forward parameter
- □   reverse parameter

and for the h parameter model become h_I, h_O, h_F and h_R.

1.2.1 Input parameter (h$_I$)

The input parameter is described in terms of input voltage (V$_{in}$) and input current (I$_{in}$) as follows:

$$h_I = \frac{V_{in}}{I_{in}}$$

As R = V/I it can be seen that h$_I$ is measured in ohms. The input parameter is, in fact, termed the *d.c. input resistance.*

1.2.2 Output parameter (h$_O$)

This parameter is described in terms of output voltage and output current as follows:

$$h_O = \frac{I_o}{V_o}$$

It can be seen that I/V is the inverse of V/I and therefore h$_O$ is a conductance (i.e. 1/R) and is measured in siemens. It is known as the *output conductance.*

1.2.3 Forward parameter (h$_F$)

This is the relationship between input current and output current as follows:

$$h_F = \frac{I_o}{I_{in}}$$

As the expression is current divided by current, h$_F$ is a ratio and therefore has no units. It is known as the *forward current gain.*

1.2.4 Reverse parameter (h$_R$)

This is the relationship between the input voltage and the output voltage as follows:

$$h_R = \frac{V_{in}}{V_o}$$

As this parameter is a voltage divided by a voltage it is a ratio, known as the *reverse voltage amplification factor*. It is the input voltage divided by the output voltage.

Note: The use of capital or lower-case letters denotes d.c. or a.c. parameters respectively. For example h_I indicates the d.c. input parameter, whereas h_r denotes the a.c. reverse parameter.

Equivalent circuits are usually employed to analyse a.c. signals, with active components shown as voltage or current generators.

Having established the h parameters for a transistor, an equivalent circuit may be produced using the four parameters. The equivalent circuit of an NPN transistor is shown in figure 1.8.

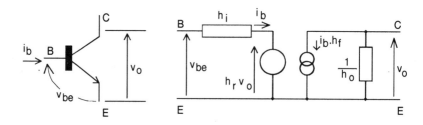

Figure 1.8 *NPN transistor equivalent circuit*

1.2.5 Transistor amplifier configurations

Three amplifier configurations are available, common-emitter, common-base and common-collector. When h parameters are applied to a particular configuration a letter is added to the parameter name. In the case of the common-emitter connection, the suffix is 'e' ('b' for base and 'c' for collector being the other two). This book will only consider the common-emitter configuration with typical values for the h parameters as follows:

h_{ie} : $2\,k\Omega$ h_{oe} : $5\,\mu S$ h_{fe} : 200 h_{re} : 10^{-4}

1.3 Circuit analysis

As the equivalent circuit will be used for a.c. analysis of the amplifier, components such as the emitter resistor and capacitor, and biasing voltages and currents are neglected. Figure 1.9 shows the circuit diagram of the common-emitter amplifier with signal conditions illustrated.

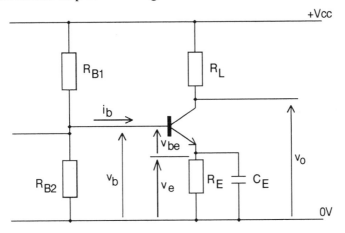

Figure 1.9 *C. E. amplifier signal conditions*

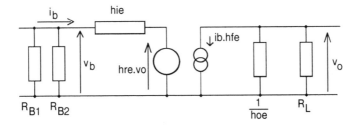

Figure 1.10 *h-parameter equivalent circuit*

Note that, for ease of analysis and later calculations, the reciprocal of h_{oe} is employed to show the output conductance as a resistance. Note also that $v_e = 0$ V and therefore, $v_b = v_{be}$.

1.3.1 Consider $h_{re}.v_o$

The typical value of h_{re} quoted (10^{-4}) is very small and, in certain circumstances, may be ignored. For example consider the following set of parameters:

If $v_b = 1$ mV then, with a voltage gain of 200, v_o would be 200 mV. With $h_{re} \approx 10^{-4}$, $h_{re}.v_o$ would be about 0.02 mV (20 μV). As a percentage of v_b, $h_{re}.v_o$ would be

$$\frac{h_{re}\, v_o \times 100\%}{v_b} = \frac{20 \times 10^{-6} \times 100\%}{1 \times 10^{-3}} = \mathbf{2\%}$$

The effect of ignoring $h_{re}.v_o$ would produce an error of approximately 2% and therefore the effects of $h_{re}.v_o$ can be neglected at this level.

A revised equivalent circuit can now be used, see figure 1.11.

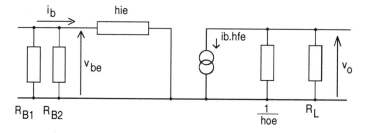

Figure 1.11 *Equivalent circuit neglecting $h_{re}.v_o$*

1.3.2 Consider $1/h_{oe}$

The output parameter, h_{oe}, also has a low value

$$h_{oe} \approx 5\ \mu S, \quad \therefore \frac{1}{h_{oe}} \approx 200\ k\Omega$$

With a typical value for R_L less than 10 kΩ, the effects of a 200 kΩ resistance in parallel will also be very small and could, under certain circumstances, be ignored.

Consider the effect of a 200 kΩ resistance connected in parallel with a 5 kΩ load resistor:

Effective resistance = $\dfrac{\text{PRODUCT}}{\text{SUM}}$

$$= \frac{200 \times 10^3 \times 5 \times 10^3}{(200 \times 10^3) + (5 \times 10^3)} = \frac{1 \times 10^9}{205 \times 10^3} = \underline{4.878 \times 10^3}$$

The difference in resistance would be 5 kΩ – 4.878 kΩ, that is 0.122 kΩ. As a percentage, the error introduced into any calculation by the omission of h_{oe} would be

$$\frac{0.122 \times 100\%}{5} = 2.44\%$$

This error is small enough to be ignored if R_L is less than 10 kΩ. As the value of R_L is increased, so is the effect of h_{oe}. The h parameter equivalent circuit is further simplified by the omission of h_{oe}, as shown in figure 1.12.

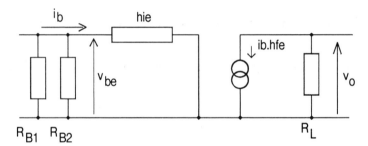

Figure 1.12 *Simplified equivalent circuit*

Example 1.1
If $h_{fe} = 100$, $h_{ie} = 1$ kΩ, $R_L = 2$ kΩ, R_B (R_{B1} // R_{B2}) = 10 kΩ and $v_b = 10$ mV, find v_o.

$$i_b = \frac{10 \times 10^{-3}}{1000} = 10\ \mu A$$

$$h_{fe}\ i_b = 10\ \mu A \times 100 = 1\ mA$$

$$v_o = h_{fe}\ i_b \times R_L = 1 \times 10^{-3} \times 2 \times 10^3$$

$$\underline{v_o = 2\ V.}$$

1.3.3 The general formula for voltage gain (A$_V$)

$$i_b = \frac{v_b}{h_{ie}} \qquad \text{------ (1)}$$

$$v_o = - h_{fe}\, i_b\, R_L \qquad \text{------ (2)}$$

substitute $i_b = v_b/h_{ie}$ into (2)

$$v_o = - \frac{h_{fe}\, v_b\, R_L}{h_{ie}}$$

As voltage gain $(A_V) = v_o/v_b$

$$A_V = \frac{v_o}{v_b} = \boxed{- \frac{h_{fe}\, R_L}{h_{ie}}}$$

Note: The minus sign indicates that the output is 180° out of phase with the input.

The expression for gain may be expressed as follows when the input is a sine wave.

$$A_V = \boxed{\frac{h_{fe}\, R_L}{h_{ie}} \ \angle\ 180°}$$

Note that the inclusion of the angle gives an expression for *COMPLEX GAIN (i.e. magnitude + direction).*

Example 1.2

If an amplifier has the following parameters: $v_b = 10$ mV, $h_{ie} = 2$ kΩ, $h_{fe} = 150$ and $R_L = 5$ kΩ, calculate the output voltage v_o.

$$A_V = - \frac{h_{fe}\, R_L}{h_{ie}} = - \frac{150 \times 5 \times 10^3}{2 \times 10^3} = -375$$

$$v_2 = A_V\, v_b = -375 \times 10 \times 10^{-3} = \underline{-3.75\ V}$$

1.3.4 Input impedance (Z$_{in}$)

The simplest method of stating the input impedance of an amplifier is 'input voltage divided by the input current', i.e.

$$Z_{in} = \frac{V_b}{i_b}$$

If the base bias resistors, R_{B1} and R_{B2} are combined to form a single resistance R_B, then the input impedance can be expressed as the base resistors in parallel with the input resistance of the transistor,

$$Z_{in} = \frac{R_B \, h_{ie}}{R_B + h_{ie}}$$

1.3.5 Output impedance (Z$_o$)

There are two possibilities when considering the output impedance,

(i) without R_L, when $Z_o = \dfrac{1}{h_{oe}}$

(ii) with R_L, when $Z_o \approx R_L$

Note that, as stated earlier, 1/h$_{oe}$ can be neglected if R$_L$ is present and has a value < 10 kΩ.

One circuit in which the value of the collector load will be high is that of the tuned-collector amplifier. This circuit is used to amplify a narrow band of frequencies, normally above the audible range, and often modulated by audio or video signals. For example, it is found in the tuning and intermediate frequency amplifiers of radio and television receivers.

If such an amplifier employs a bi-polar transistor, the collector circuit comprises a parallel tuned circuit whose impedance, or dynamic resistance, will be very high at its frequency of operation (resonance). The output resistance of the transistor ($1/h_{oe}$) becomes significant in these circumstances and must be taken into account when analysing the performance of the circuit.

1.4 The tuned-collector amplifier

Tuned circuits may be series or parallel circuit arrangements. In this text only the parallel tuned circuit will be considered. This circuit has a very high impedance at its resonant frequency and, if the circuit is arranged as the output load of an amplifier, produces a high gain at that frequency.

Consider a perfect inductor and a perfect capacitor, i.e. with no losses, connected in parallel, as in figure 1.13.

At the frequency of operation (f_o), i.e. at resonance, i_C and i_L are equal, but are in anti-phase, therefore $i_s = 0$.

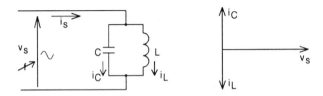

Figure 1.13 *Ideal parallel L-C circuit*

Plots of current against frequency and impedance against frequency would reveal responses as shown in figure 1.14.

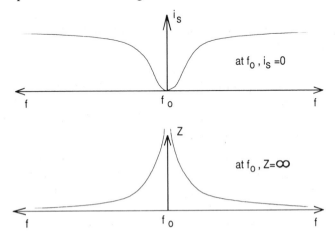

Figure 1.14 *Plots of current and impedance*

If practical components, i.e. components with losses, are considered then the losses of both capacitor and inductor may be considered as a single resistance in series with the perfect inductor. In this case, at resonance, some current will flow in the inductor, producing the circuit and phasor diagrams as illustrated in figure 1.14.

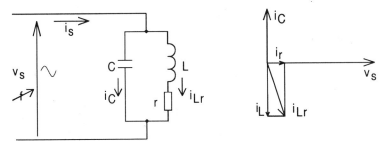

Figure 1.15 *Parallel tuned circuit with series R*

Graphs of current and impedance against frequency now show the minimum value of i_s to be greater than 0, and the value of Z_{max} to be less than ∞.

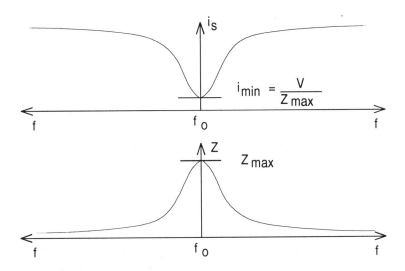

Figure 1.16 *Practical circuit responses*

Z_{max} is the impedance of the circuit at its resonant frequency, f_o. It is termed 'dynamic impedance' and identified by the symbols Z_D or Z_o.

However, the dynamic impedance is purely resistive at resonance and is often called 'dynamic resistance', R_D or R_o.

The value of R_D is determined by the values of L, C and r:

$$R_D = \frac{L}{C\,r}$$

Example 1.3

$L = 10\,mH, r = 50\,\Omega$ and $C = 25\,nF$. Calculate R_D and the resonant frequency, f_o, of the circuit.

$$R_D = \frac{10 \times 10^{-3}}{25 \times 10^{-9} \times 50}$$

$$R_D = \frac{10 \times 10^{-3} \times 10^9}{25 \times 50} = \frac{10^7}{1250}$$

$$\underline{R_D = 8\,k\Omega}$$

$$f_o = \frac{1}{2\pi\sqrt{L\,C}}$$

$$f_o = \frac{1}{2\pi\sqrt{10 \times 10^{-3} \times 25 \times 10^{-9}}}$$

$$f_o = \frac{1}{2\pi\sqrt{250 \times 10^{-12}}}$$

$$f_o = \frac{10^6}{2\pi \times 15.81} = \textbf{10.0658 kHz.}$$

$$\underline{f_o \approx \textbf{10.07 kHz.}}$$

An alternative method of representing the practical tuned circuit at resonance is to show a perfect L-C circuit shunted by the loss impedance at f_o. This arrangement produces an equivalent circuit that is similar to those already used for wideband amplifiers but with L and C in parallel with R_D, see figure 1.17.

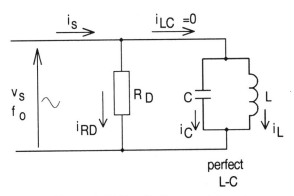

Figure 1.17 *Parallel loss resistance*

At f_o, $i_{RD} = i_s$ (as $i_{LC} = 0$).

Remember that the perfect L-C circuit draws no current at resonance.

1.4.1 Q-factor

The Q-factor of a capacitor or inductor is a measure of its quality and can be expressed as the ratio of reactive current to source current. At resonance, $i_C = i_L$, therefore

$$Q = \frac{i_C}{i_s} \quad \text{or} \quad Q = \frac{i_L}{i_s}$$

since $i_s = i_{RD}$

$$Q = \frac{i_C}{i_{RD}} = \frac{\dfrac{v_s}{X_C}}{\dfrac{v_s}{R_D}}$$

$$Q = \frac{v_s}{X_C} \times \frac{R_D}{v_s} = \frac{R_D}{X_C}$$

But $X_C = \dfrac{1}{\omega C}$ (from $X_C = \dfrac{1}{2\pi f C}$)

$$Q = \frac{R_D}{\dfrac{1}{\omega C}}$$

$$Q = R_D \, \omega \, C$$

When this tuned circuit is connected into the collector circuit of a transistor amplifier, another resistance is connected in parallel with R_D, namely $1/h_{oe}$.

The tuned collector amplifier, with the L-C parallel tuned circuit as previously examined, is shown in figure 1.18.

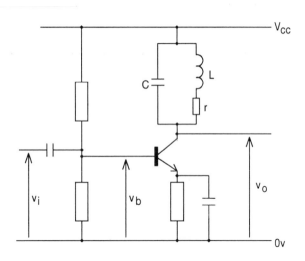

Figure 1.18 *Tuned collector amplifier*

The equivalent circuit is shown in figure 1.19 and shows the practical tuned circuit of L, C and R_D shunted by the output resistance of the transistor, $1/h_{oe}$. If R_D in parallel with $1/h_{oe}$ is referred to as R_T, then the Q factor of this circuit is calculated from

$$Q = R_T \, \omega \, C$$

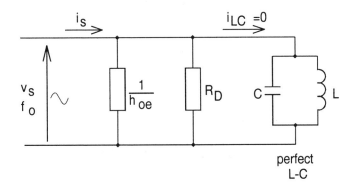

Figure 1.18 *Tuned circuit shunted by 1/h*oe

The equivalent circuit can then be simplified to that illustrated in figure 1.19.

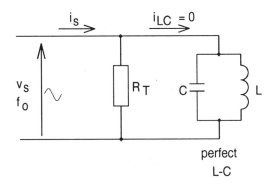

Figure 1.19 *Simplified circuit*

Example 1.4

$R_D = 8\ k\Omega, \dfrac{1}{h_{oe}} = 50\ k\Omega, f_o = 10\ kHz$ *and* $C = 25\ nF$, *calculate Q*.

$$Q = 2\pi\ f_o\ C\ R_T$$

$$R_T = R_D\ \|\ \frac{1}{h_{oe}}$$

$$Q = 2\pi \times 10 \times 10^3 \times (8000 \parallel 50000) \times 25 \times 10^{-9}$$

$$\underline{Q = 10.83}$$

Example 1.5

$R_D = 10\ k\Omega$, $1/h_{oe} = 60\ k\Omega$, $f_o = 20\ kHz$ and $C = 100\ nF$, calculate Q.

$$\underline{R_T = 8.57\,k\Omega \quad : \quad Q = 107.7}$$

The full equivalent circuit of the tuned collector amplifier at f_o is illustrated in figure 1.20.

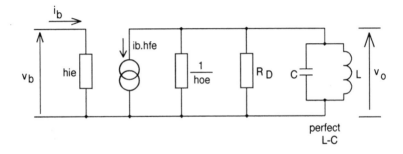

Figure 1.20 *Full equivalent circuit*

The Q factor for the amplifier can be derived from the same expression as that for the tuned circuit alone if the parallel resistances, $1/h_{oe}$ and R_D are treated as a single resistance R_T. The expression for the Q of the tuned circuit is

$$Q_{LCr} = \omega C R_D$$

However, the Q-factor for the amplifier is

$$Q_{AMP} = \omega C R_T$$

but $R_T = R_D$ in parallel with $1/h_{oe}$, so

$$R_T = \frac{[\, R_D \, \frac{1}{h_{oe}} \,]}{[\, R_D + \frac{1}{h_{oe}} \,]}$$

multiply top and bottom by hoe

$$R_T = \frac{R_D}{[\, R_D \, h_{oe} + 1 \,]}$$

$$Q_{AMP} = \omega \, C \, \frac{R_D}{[\, R_D \, h_{oe} + 1 \,]}$$

Where component values are available this formula is fine. However, if the Q of the tuned circuit is known, a simpler formula is available

$$Q_{LCr} = \omega \, C \, R_D$$

$$Q_{AMP} = \frac{Q_{LCr}}{(\, R_D \, h_{oe} + 1 \,)}$$

Example 1.6

If $Q_{LCr} = 15$, $h_{oe} = 5 \ \mu S$ and $R_D = 10 \ k\Omega$, calculate Q_{AMP}.

$$Q_{AMP} = \frac{15}{(10 \times 10^3 \times 5 \times 10^{-6}) + 1}$$

$$Q_{AMP} = \frac{15}{(5 \times 10^{-2}) + 1}$$

$$Q_{AMP} = \frac{15}{1.05} = \underline{\textbf{14.29}}$$

The expression for the gain of the amplifier may be developed in the same manner as the wide band amplifier discussed earlier in this chapter. The use of the equivalent circuit, figure 1.21, is beneficial.

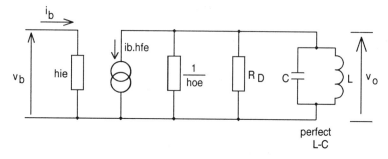

Figure 1.21 *Equivalent circuit*

$$\text{voltage gain} \ = \ \frac{V_o}{V_b}$$

At resonance, i_L and i_C equal zero, therefore the effective output resistance is R_D in parallel with $1/h_{oe}$, so

$$V_o \ = \ - h_{fe} \ i_b \ R_T$$

$$V_o \ = \ - \ \frac{h_{fe} \ i_b \ R_D}{(R_D \ h_{oe} \ + 1)} \quad \text{and} \quad V_b \ = \ h_{ie} \ i_b$$

$$A_v \ = \ \frac{V_o}{V_b} \ = \ - \ \frac{\dfrac{h_{fe} \ i_b \ R_D}{(R_D \ h_{oe} \ + 1)}}{h_{ie} \ i_b}$$

$$A_v \ = \ - \ \frac{h_{fe} \ i_b \ R_D}{h_{ie} \ i_b \ (R_D \ h_{oe} \ + 1)}$$

the i_bs cancel, so

$$A_v \ (f_o \ ) \ = \ - \ \frac{h_{fe} \ R_D}{h_{ie} \ (R_D \ h_{oe} \ + 1)}$$

Example 1.7

If $h_{fe} = 100$, $h_{ie} = 2$ kΩ, $R_D = 10$ kΩ and $h_{oe} = 5$ μS, calculate $A_{v(fo)}$.

$$A_v(f_o) = - \frac{100 \times 10 \times 10^3}{2 \times 10^3 ((5 \times 10^{-6} \times 10 \times 10^3) + 1)}$$

$$A_v(f_o) = - \frac{10^6}{2 \times 10^3 \times 1.05}$$

$$\underline{A_v(f_o) = 476.2 \angle 180°}$$

Example 1.8

If $h_{fe} = 150$, $h_{ie} = 1$ kΩ, $R_D = 20$ kΩ and $h_{oe} = 10$ μS, calculate $A_{v(fo)}$.

$$A_v(f_o) = - \frac{150 \times 10 \times 10^3}{1 \times 10^3 ((10 \times 10^{-6} \times 20 \times 10^3) + 1)}$$

$$A_v(f_o) = - \frac{1.5 \times 10^6}{1 \times 10^3 \times 1.2}$$

$$\underline{A_v(f_o) = 1250 \angle 180°}$$

2 Cascaded Amplifiers

In many applications, for example audio or radio-frequency amplifiers, it is unlikely that sufficient voltage gain can be achieved with a single transistor amplifier. In order to obtain additional gain, two or more amplifier stages may be 'cascaded' together, as shown in figure 2.1.

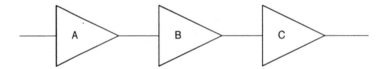

Figure 2.1 *Cascaded amplifiers*

If the voltage gain (A_v) of each amplifier is expressed as a numeric ratio then the overall gain of the system is the *product* of the individual gains.

Example 2.1

Gain A = 100, Gain B = 60, Gain C = 20

overall gain = 100 x 60 x 20 = 120,000

If, however, each amplifier's gain is expressed as a logarithmic ratio (i.e. in dBs) then the overall amplification of the system is the *sum* of the individual gains.

Example 2.2

gain A = 40 dB, gain B = 35.563 dB, gain C = 26.021 dB

overall gain = 40 + 35.563 + 26.021   = 101.584 dB

Note: To convert a numeric voltage ratio into the logarithmic form use

$$A_v (dB) = 20 \log_{10} A_v$$

and to convert a logarithmic voltage ratio into numeric form use

$$A_v = 10^{\left(\frac{A_v (dB)}{20} \right)}$$

Each amplifier is described as a 'stage' of amplification and various circuit arrangements are available for performing inter-stage coupling. The main requirements of inter-stage coupling are

(i) good a.c. signal coupling

(ii) effective 'blocking' of the bias/quiescent (d.c.) conditions

Transformer, direct coupling and resistance-capacitance circuits are the most popular methods, each having advantages and disadvantages compared with the others. These means of coupling will be examined in turn, with particular emphasis being placed on R-C coupling.

2.1 Transformer coupling

Transformer coupling provides perfect d.c. blocking and good impedance matching. However, for wide band, audio or low frequency operation, the value of inductance required makes the size and weight of the transformer large, and therefore, impractical. In addition, such transformers are considerably more expensive than components required for the other forms of inter-stage coupling mentioned.

For high frequency work, though, the transformer is a highly efficient and practical method of coupling. The use of transformers with tuned primary and secondary windings allows a narrow band of frequencies to be coupled, providing a means of rejecting signals at unwanted frequencies. The use of transformers for inter-stage coupling also allows the circuit designer to match the output impedance of one stage to the input of the next. This method provides a high degree of impedance matching and, in turn, a high level of power transfer occurs.

For tuned amplifiers, greater selectivity is obtained if both primary and secondary windings of the transformer are tuned, as shown in figure 2.2.

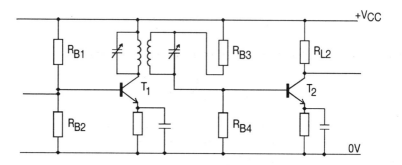

2.2 Transformer-coupled amplifiers

The arrangement shown is perfectly valid, with maximum power transfer achieved by matching the impedance of the winding to its appropriate circuit. However, in many miniature circuits, the capacitor is a very small, fixed-value component and tuning is achieved by means of one or two variable-position cores in the transformer. Both the transformer and the capacitors would be enclosed in a screening can, with access, if required, to the tuning 'slug'. Impedance matching in this case would require the use of a 'tapped' winding, as shown in figure 2.3.

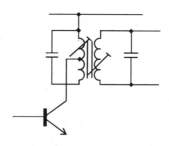

2.3 Typical tuned-circuit coupling

2.2 Direct coupling

In this method of inter-stage coupling there is *no* d.c. blocking between stages. This means that the bias conditions of one stage will affect those of the next and, therefore, careful component selection is required in order to satisfy the operating conditions of both stages.

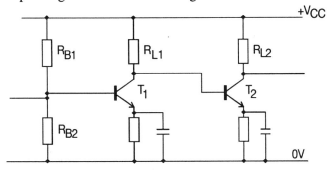

Figure 2.4 *Directly coupled amplifier stages*

The arrangement shown in figure 2.4, in which the base of T_2 is connected directly to the collector of T_1, presents problems for the biasing of T_2. This may be overcome by using a potential divider network between the two transistors, but a loss of gain will result from this 'cure'.

Another method for overcoming the biasing problem is to drive a PNP transistor from an NPN. This idea can be extended so that a series of transistors, alternating between NPN and PNP types can be directly coupled.

As seen from the frequency response curve shown in figure 2.5, the directly-coupled amplifier gives a virtually linear response from d.c. up to high frequencies. At that point, stray capacitance in the base region of T_2 produces a roll-off in gain. This effect is the same as that experienced by an R-C coupled amplifier at high frequencies and will be dealt with under that heading.

One major advantage of the directly-coupled arrangement is that very slowly changing d.c. signals may be amplified. This includes the output from a range of sensors, used to monitor changes in physical quantities, e.g. light, temperature, humidity, water quality, etc.

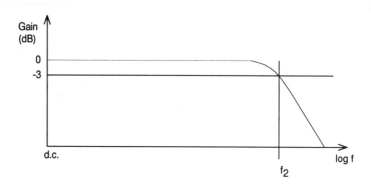

Figure 2.5 *Directly-coupled amplifier response*

Note: These signals could not be amplified by a transformer-coupled or an R-C coupled amplifier because the d.c. content of the signal would be blocked by the coupling components.

The excellent low frequency response of directly-coupled amplifiers leads to their extensive use in high quality audio amplifiers. In addition, their ability to accept and amplify slowly changing d.c. signals means that they are to be found in many instrument amplifiers.

A disadvantage of the direct coupling method is that of component drift. If a transistor becomes warm and, as a result, its biasing arrangement changes, that change will appear at the input of the next stage and will be amplified along with any required signal. This problem is reduced in practical circuits by the use of low drift stages such as the long-tailed pair (described in chapter 4). A further problem with d.c. connection is that each stage of amplification is dependent upon the previous stage for its biasing conditions. Any major change, due, for example, to component failure, could result in unsuitable bias being provided.

Note: A practical manifestation of unsuitable bias, and one that is likely to be encountered by technicians, is that a semiconductor device that develops a fault may well upset the d.c. conditions around it to the extent that faults occur in devices connected to it. If many stages of amplification are directly connected then a 'knock-on' effect could take place right through to the power output stage. This could result in the failure of a large number of semiconductor devices.

2.3 R-C coupling

The main advantage of R-C coupling is that good d.c. blocking between stages is obtained while the alternating signal is allowed through virtually unhindered. This allows each stage to be biased without consideration of that following. The relatively high d.c. content in the output circuit of the first stage does not interfere with the next. Similarly, the base bias requirements of the second transistor do not influence the collector circuit of the first. In addition, R-C coupling requires only inexpensive components.

The main disadvantage of this arrangement is the presence, at low frequencies, of a considerable amount of capacitive reactance in series with the signal, making the R-C coupled amplifier unsuitable for very low frequency a.c. or slowly varying d.c. signals. This reactance increases as the frequency of the applied signal decreases, as seen from the expression

$$X_C = \frac{1}{2\pi f C}$$

The reactance forms one section of an attenuator network, reducing the signal that is applied to the next stage, see figure 2.6.

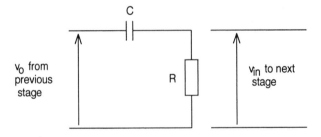

Figure 2.6 *R-C coupling arrangements*

Figure 2.6 shows the arrangement of R and C for this mode of inter-stage coupling. Clearly the ratio between the reactance of C and the resistance of R will determine what percentage of the output of one stage of amplification is passed on to the next. As the reactance of C varies with the frequency of the applied signal, so will the amount of signal passed on.

A more detailed examination of this subject will be undertaken later in this chapter.

The addition of a second stage of amplification will lower the load resistance connected across the output of the first stage, reducing its gain. In order to determine accurately the effects of this additional loading it is necessary to consider 'stage gain', where a stage is defined as being from the base of one transistor to the base of the next. In the circuit shown in figure 2.7, the stage gain is v_3 / v_1 .

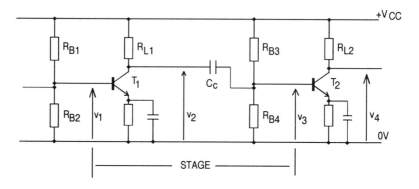

Figure 2.7 *R-C coupled amplifier*

Typical circuit values and transistor parameters for a wide band (e.g. 20 Hz to 1 MHz) amplifier might be:

R_{L1}: 5 kΩ R_{B3}: 100 kΩ R_{B4}: 10 kΩ h_{ie}: 2 kΩ C_c: 10 µF
h_{fe}: 100 C_s (input capacitance of T_2):   200 pF

The small signal h-parameter equivalent circuit is used in order to derive an expression for the voltage gain of a stage of amplification.

Note that the emitter components are not included in this equivalent circuit as they have no effect on the small a.c. signals that are being considered. Also, although C_s is low in value, typically in the order of a few hundred picofarads, its effect at high frequencies will be significant.

The equivalent circuit (figure 2.8) shows the physical capacitor C_c, and the stray capacitance that forms C_s. As already mentioned, C_c affects the performance of the amplifier at low frequencies. The stray capacitance, effectively in parallel with h_{ie} of T_2 and therefore shunting the signal, affects the performance at high frequencies.

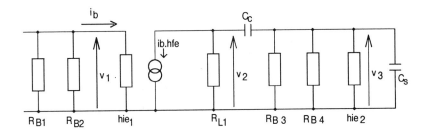

Figure 2.8 *R-C coupled amplifier equivalent circuit*

Example 2.3

If $R_{L1} = 4.7$ kΩ, $R_{B3} = 100$ kΩ, $R_{B4} = 10$ kΩ, $h_{ie2} = 2$ kΩ and $C_s = 250$ pF, calculate the percentage loss in gain at 1 MHz due to the presence of C_s.

The effective output load resistance without C_s =

$$4.7\,k\Omega \; /\!/ \; 100\,k\Omega \; /\!/ \; 10\,k\Omega \; /\!/ \; 2\,k\Omega \; = \; \textbf{\textit{1.215 k}}\Omega$$

The reactance of C_s at 1 MHz =

$$\frac{1}{2\pi \times 10^6 \times 250 \times 10^{-12}} = \textbf{\textit{636.6}}\,\Omega$$

As the R and C components form a parallel circuit with a common voltage across them, the impedance triangle is formed with the inverse of resistance, reactance and impedance (see figure 2.9).

The effective output load resistance including C_s (i.e. the circuit impedance Z) is found from

$$\frac{1}{Z} = \sqrt{\left(\frac{1}{X_C}\right)^2 + \left(\frac{1}{R}\right)^2} \quad , \text{i.e.} \; \textbf{\textit{Z} = 563.9}\,\Omega$$

Therefore the signal lost in C_s is

$$100 - (\frac{563.9}{1215.4} \times 100) \% = \mathbf{53.6\%}$$

Clearly such a loss cannot be ignored and further consideration of the effects of C_s will follow later in this chapter.

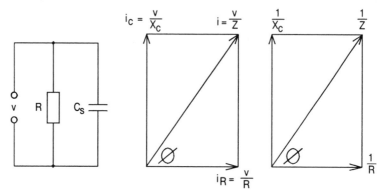

Figure 2.9 *Impedance triangle*

If a graph was plotted of amplifier gain against log of frequency it would illustrate the effects of the coupling capacitor, C_c, and the stray capacitance, C_s. Such a plot, as in figure 2.10, would show that there is a range of frequencies, from $10f_1$ up to $0.1f_2$, where the effects of the two capacitances are negligible. This range of frequencies is called 'Mid band'. The frequency band below Mid band is known as 'Low band' and those frequencies above Mid band are said to be in 'High band'.

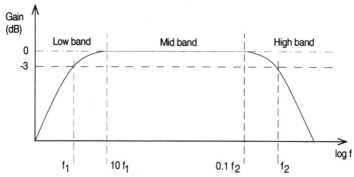

Figure 2.10 *Gain/frequency plot*

Note: The vertical axis (gain) is always shown in dB, and the horizontal axis (frequency) is always the logarithm of frequency 'log f'. This method of axis labelling is adopted because of the human ear's response to changes in both amplitude and frequency. It is well-established that the ear's responses to such changes are not linear but logarithmic. In practical terms, for example, the potentiometer used to control sound 'volume' on an audio amplifier will have a logarithmic resistance characteristic.

Later in this chapter it will be shown that the 'roll-off' rate at each end of the amplifier's response is 20 dB per decade (in the linear sections).

Analysis of the circuit at frequencies in each of the three bands will now take place in order to develop expressions for amplifier gain. The first frequency to be selected will be in mid band so that the effects of C_c and C_s will have negligible effect upon the analysis.

2.3.1 Analysis at 1 kHz (Typical mid band frequency)

The reactance of the coupling capacitor at 1 kHz will be very low in comparison with other circuit resistances. As this low reactance is in series with the signal its effect will be very small.

Example 2.4

Consider a 10 μF inter-stage coupling capacitor

$$X_C = \frac{1}{2\pi f C} = \frac{1}{2\pi \times 10^3 \times 10 \times 10^{-6}} = \frac{10^2}{2\pi} \, \Omega$$

$$\underline{X_C = 15.9 \, \Omega}$$

It can be seen that , when compared with, for example, the output load resistance (R_{L1}), the reactance of C_c is negligible.

For the same frequency, the reactance of the stray capacitance will be very high. However, this reactance is applied in shunt with the signal and will also have no appreciable effect.

Example 2.5

If C_s equals 250 pF then

$$X_C = \frac{1}{2\pi f C} = \frac{1}{2\pi \times 10^3 \times 250 \times 10^{-12}} = \frac{10^9}{1.5708}\Omega$$

$$\underline{X_C = 636.62\,k\Omega}$$

This is clearly a very large value when compared with the effective input resistance of stage 2 (1.215 kΩ) and may be neglected.

The analysis of the amplifier in mid band is again performed with a small signal h-parameter equivalent circuit. The equivalent circuit for mid band operation is shown in figure 2.11. As C_c is a series component it is shown as a short-circuit and C_s is shown as an open-circuit.

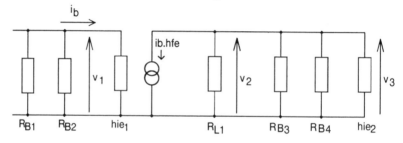

Figure 2.11 *Mid band equivalent circuit*

Note that with C_C treated as a short-circuit, $v_2 = v_3$.

It can be clearly seen that the output load resistance is made up of four resistors connected in parallel. For ease of analysis, the circuit may be simplified by treating all four parallel resistors, R_{L1}, R_{B3}, R_{B4} and h_{ie2} as one, R_p (see figure 2.12).

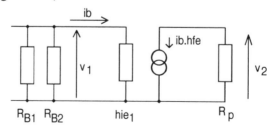

Figure 2.12 *Simplified circuit*

Example 2.6

$$R_{L1} = 5\ k\Omega, \qquad R_{B3} = 100\ k\Omega, \qquad R_{B4} = 10\ k\Omega, \qquad h_{ie2} = 2\ k\Omega$$

$$\underline{R_p = 1.23\ k\Omega}$$

Note: Remember that the effective resistance of several resistors in parallel is always *less than* the lowest resistor value.

The expression for mid band gain becomes almost identical to that for a single-stage amplifier, with R_p in place of R_L, i.e.

$$\text{Mid band gain } (A_M) = \frac{h_{fe}\ R_p}{h_{ie}} \angle 180°$$

Example 2.7
A transistor has the following parameters:
  h_{ie}: 2 kΩ h_{fe}: 200 h_{re} and h_{oe}: negligible
If $R_{L1} = 2\ k\Omega$, $R_{B3} = 100\ k\Omega$ and $R_{B4} = 15\ k\Omega$, calculate:
  (a) the gain of the amplifier.
  (b) the stage gain with an identical stage added.

$$(a)\ \ A_v = -\frac{h_{fe}\ R_{L1}}{h_{ie}} = -\frac{200 \times 2 \times 10^3}{2 \times 10^3}$$

$$\underline{A_v = 200 \angle\ 180°}$$

$$(b)\ \ A_M = -\frac{h_{fe}\ R_p}{h_{ie}}$$

$$R_p = R_{L1}, R_{B3}, R_{B4}\ and\ h_{ie2}\ in\ parallel$$

$$R_p = 928.8\ \Omega$$

$$A_M = -\frac{200 \times 928.8}{2 \times 10^3}$$

$$\underline{A_M = 92.88 \angle\ 180°}$$

2.3.2 Analysis for high band operation

At frequencies above mid band, i.e. in high band, the reactance of the input capacitance of the next stage, C_s, begins to fall. As it falls it draws sufficient current from $h_{fe}.i_b$ to affect the performance of the circuit. Any reduction in the current in R_p will reduce the voltage developed across it, thereby reducing stage gain.

By using the simplified equivalent circuit from the previous work on mid band gain, the high band equivalent circuit is obtained by adding C_s across R_p, illustrated in figure 2.13.

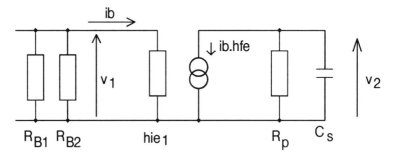

Figure 2.13 *High band equivalent circuit*

Further simplification can be achieved if R_p and X_{Cs} are combined into Z_p as shown in figure 2.14.

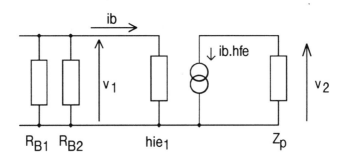

Figure 2.14 *Simplified equivalent circuit*

Deriving the expression for high band gain (A_H)

$$A_H = \frac{v_2}{v_1}$$

$$v_1 = i_b h_{ie1}$$

$$v_2 = -h_{fe} i_b Z_p$$

$$A_H = \frac{-h_{fe} i_b Z_p}{i_b h_{ie1}}$$

i_bs cancel out so ...

$$A_H = \frac{-h_{fe} Z_p}{h_{ie1}}$$

However, $Z_p = R_p // X_{Cs}$, which is a complex quantity, i.e. it comprises magnitude and phase, therefore 'j notation' will be used to determine the value of Z_p.

$$X_{Cs} = \frac{1}{j \omega C_s}$$

$$Z_p = \frac{R_p \dfrac{1}{j \omega C_s}}{R_p + \dfrac{1}{j \omega C_s}} \qquad \left(\frac{\text{PRODUCT}}{\text{SUM}} \right)$$

Multiply top and bottom of the expression by $j\omega C_s$

$$Z_p = \frac{R_p}{j \omega C_s R_p + 1}$$

$$\boxed{A_H = - \frac{h_{fe} R_p}{h_{ie1} (1 + j \omega C_s R_p)}}$$

This expression should be used if high band gain is to be calculated directly from component values. However, if A_M has already been calculated then

$$\frac{-h_{fe}\,R_p}{h_{ie1}} = A_M \quad \text{may be used in the expression for } A_H, \text{ giving}$$

$$A_H = \frac{A_M}{1 + j\,\omega\,C_s\,R_p}$$

Example 2.8

If $A_M = 100\,\angle 180°$, $R_{L1} = 5\ k\Omega$, $R_B = 10\ k\Omega$, $h_{ie2} = 2\ k\Omega$ and $C_s = 100\ pF$, calculate the gain at 10 kHz, 100 kHz, 1 MHz and 10 MHz.

$$A_H = \frac{A_M}{1 + j\,\omega\,C_s\,R_p}$$

$R_p = R_{L1}$, R_B and h_{ie2} in parallel

$$R_p = 1.25\ k\Omega$$

At 10 kHz

$$A_H = \frac{A_M}{1 + j\,(\,2\,\pi \times 10^4 \times 100 \times 10^{-12} \times 1.25 \times 10^3)}$$

$$A_H = \frac{A_M}{1 + j\,(7.854 \times 10^{-3})}$$

$$\underline{A_H = 100\,\angle\,179.55°}$$

Note: It is clear that 10 kHz is, in fact, in mid band for this amplifier.

At 100 kHz

Instead of re-working the complete expression for A_H, a short-cut may be employed. The frequency for this calculation is a factor of 10 larger than for the last, and therefore the imaginary part or 'j' value will also be 10 times larger, hence

$$A_H = \frac{A_M}{1 + j\,(7.854 \times 10^{-2})}$$

$$\underline{A_H = 100 \angle 175.54°}$$

At 1 MHz

Again, 'j' is increased by a factor of 10, so

$$A_H = \frac{A_M}{1 + j\,(7.854 \times 10^{-1})}$$

$$\underline{A_H = 79 \angle 142°}$$

At 10 MHz

$$A_H = \frac{A_M}{1 + j\,7.854}$$

$$\underline{A_H = 12.63 \angle 97.3°}$$

2.3.3 Prediction of the upper 3dB frequency (f2)

It may be desirable to predict the upper 3 dB frequency of an amplifier stage from component values.

When the gain is 3 dB down on mid band gain, the output voltage will have

fallen to 0.707 $\left(\frac{1}{\sqrt{2}}\right)$ times its mid band value.

$$\frac{A_M}{\sqrt{2}} = A_{-3dB}$$

$$\text{But } A_H = \frac{A_M}{1 + j\,\omega\,C_s\,R_p}$$

$$\text{So, at } f_2, \ \frac{A_M}{\sqrt{2}} = \frac{A_M}{1 + j\,\omega_2\,C_s\,R_p}$$

A_Ms cancel, leaving $\sqrt{2} = 1 + j\,\omega_2\,C_s\,R_p$

It is known that, in terms of magnitude only, $\sqrt{2} = \sqrt{(1^2 + 1^2)}$, therefore, by substitution $(\omega_2\,C_s\,R_p)$ must equal 1

$$\text{and } \omega_2 = \frac{1}{C_s\,R_p}$$

$$f_2 = \frac{1}{2\,\pi\,C_s\,R_p}$$

Example 2.9

Using previous values, i.e. $A_M = 100$, $R_{L1} = 5\ k\Omega$, $R_B = 10\ k\Omega$, $h_{ie2} = 2\ k\Omega$ and $C_s = 100\ pF$, calculate f_2.

$$\boldsymbol{R_p = 1.25\ k\Omega}$$

$$f_2 = \frac{1}{2\pi\,C_s\,R_p}$$

$$f_2 = \frac{1}{2\pi \times 100 \times 10^{-12} \times 1.25 \times 10^{3}}$$

$$\underline{f_2 = 1.27\ \textbf{MHz.}}$$

2.3.4 Calculation of roll-off rate

In order to calculate the rate of high-frequency roll-off, we must be sure that the slope we are using is beyond the curve and into the straight-line area. The decade between 10 MHz and 100 MHz would be more linear than, say, that between 1 MHz and 10 MHz.

$$\underline{\textit{Gain at 100 MHz} \; = \; \textit{1.273} \; \angle \; \textit{90.8}°}$$

The slope of the gain roll-off is usually quoted in dB, therefore the two gain values must be converted into dB form.

$$\text{voltage gain (dB)} \; = \; 20 \log_{10} A_v$$

$$\text{So, at 10 MHz, Gain (dB)} \; = \; 20 \log_{10} 12.63 \; = \; 22.03 \text{ dB}$$

$$\text{and at 100 MHz, Gain (dB)} \; = \; 20 \log_{10} 1.273 \; = \; 2.096 \text{ dB}$$

$$\underline{\textbf{Slope} \; = \; \textbf{22.03} - \textbf{2.10} \; = \; \textbf{19.93 dB}}$$

This value should be 20dB, as that is the known roll-off rate (at high and low frequencies) for this type of amplifier (i.e. a first order system).

Note that as the frequency has risen to a point where voltage gain approaches unity (100 MHz), the phase angle is approaching 90°.

2.3.5 Analysis for low band operation

In low band, the coupling capacitor, C_c, affects the gain of the circuit and must, therefore, be considered in the equivalent circuit for low band operation, as illustrated in figure 2.15.

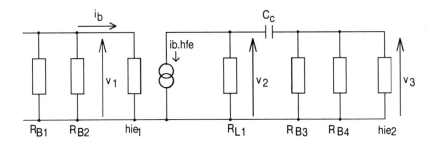

Figure 2.15 *Low band equivalent circuit*

$$\text{low band gain}\,(\,A_L\,) \;=\; \frac{v3}{v1}$$

If all of the resistances connected across the input of T_2 are combined into a single resistance called R_{in2}, then a simplified equivalent circuit may be employed, see figure 2.16.

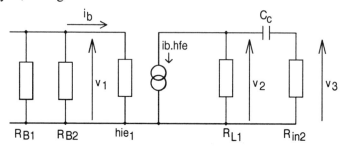

Figure 2.16 *Simplified equivalent circuit*

$$R_{in2} \;=\; R_{B3}\,/\!/\,R_{B4}\,/\!/\,h_{ie2}$$

Note that R_{in2} does not equal R_p!

Deriving the expression for low band gain (A_L)

The current, $i_b.h_{fe}$, is divided into two paths, one through R_{L1}, the other through X_{Cc} in series with R_{in2}. The ratio of the two currents is determined by the relationship between the impedance of each 'leg'. Consider the circuit shown in figure 2.17.

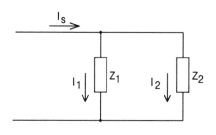

Figure 2.17 *Current dividing network*

I_s is split between I_1 and I_2 according to the ratios,

$$I_1 \;=\; I_s\left(\frac{Z_2}{Z_1+Z_2}\right)$$

$$I_2 \;=\; I_s\left(\frac{Z_1}{Z_1+Z_2}\right)$$

In the amplifier under consideration, $Z_1 = R_{L1}$ and $Z_2 = X_{Cc} + h_{ie2}$.
Then,

$$i_3 = h_{fe}\, i_b\, \frac{R_{L1}}{\left(R_{L1} + R_{in2} + \dfrac{1}{j\,\omega\,C_c}\right)}$$

$$\text{and} \quad v_3 = -i_3\, R_{in2}$$

$$\text{so} \quad v_3 = \frac{-h_{fe}\, i_b\, R_{L1}\, R_{in2}}{\left(R_{L1} + R_{in2} + \dfrac{1}{j\,\omega\,C_c}\right)}$$

To make the final expression simpler, it is helpful if the formula can be expressed in terms of R_p (R_p was the term used for all resistances when C_c had no effect on the circuit. It is $R_{L1} \; // \; R_{in2}$).

Divide top and bottom by $(R_{L1} + R_{in2})$

$$v_3 = \frac{-h_{fe}\, i_b\, \dfrac{R_{L1}\, R_{in2}}{(R_{L1} + R_{in2})}}{\left[\dfrac{R_{L1}}{(R_{L1} + R_{in2})} + \dfrac{R_{in2}}{(R_{L1} + R_{in2})} + \dfrac{1}{j\,\omega\,C_c\,(R_{L1} + R_{in2})}\right]}$$

As $\dfrac{R_{L1}}{(R_{L1} + R_{in2})} + \dfrac{R_{in2}}{(R_{L1} + R_{in2})} = 1$ and $R_p = \dfrac{R_{L1}\, R_{in2}}{(R_{L1} + R_{in2})}$

$$v_3 = \frac{-h_{fe1}\, i_b\, R_p}{\left[1 + \dfrac{1}{j\,\omega\,C_c\,(R_{L1} + R_{in2})}\right]}$$

but voltage gain $= v_3 / v_1$ and $v_1 = i_b\, h_{ie1}$

$$A_L = \frac{v_3}{v_1} = \frac{\dfrac{-h_{fe1}\, i_b\, R_p}{\left[1 + \dfrac{1}{j\,\omega\,C_c\,(R_{L1} + R_{in2})}\right]}}{i_b\, h_{ie1}}$$

$$A_L = \frac{-h_{fe1}\,R_p}{h_{ie1}\left[1 + \dfrac{1}{j\,\omega\,C_c\,(R_{L1} + R_{in2})}\right]}$$

$$\text{but } \frac{-h_{fe}\,R_p}{h_{ie1}} = A_M\text{, so}$$

$$A_L = \frac{A_M}{\left[1 + \dfrac{1}{j\,\omega\,C_c\,(R_{L1} + R_{in2})}\right]}$$

Example 2.10

If $A_M = 100\,\angle 180°$, $R_{L1} = 5\ k\Omega$, $h_{ie2} = 2\ k\Omega$, $R_B = 10\ k\Omega$ and $C_c = 1\ \mu F$, calculate the gain at 1 kHz, 100 Hz and 10 Hz.

At 1 kHz

$$A_L = \frac{100\,\angle\,180°}{1 + \dfrac{1}{j\,2\,\pi \times 10^3 \times 10^{-6} \times 6670}}$$

$$A_L = \frac{100\,\angle\,180°}{1 + \dfrac{1}{j\,(2\,\pi \times 6.67)}}$$

As $1/j = -j$ then

$$so, \quad A_L = \frac{100\,\angle\,180°}{1 - j\,\dfrac{1}{2\pi \times 6.67}}$$

$$A_L = \frac{100\,\angle\,180°}{1 - j\,0.024}$$

$$\underline{\boldsymbol{A_L = 100\,\angle\,180°}} \qquad A_L\,(dB) = 20\,log_{10}\,A_M \quad \underline{\boldsymbol{= 40\ dB}}$$

At 100 Hz

As the frequency is 10 times smaller, the 'j' quantity is 10 times larger, and...

$$A_L = \frac{100 \angle 180°}{1 - j\,0.24}$$

$A_L = 97.2 \angle 193.5°$ $A_L\,(dB) = 20\,log_{10}\,A_M$ **$= 39.75\,dB$**

At 10 Hz

Similarly,

$$A_L = \frac{100 \angle 180°}{1 - j\,2.4}$$

$A_L = 38.46 \angle 247.4°$ $A_L\,(dB) = 20\,log_{10}\,A_M$ **$= 31.7\,dB$**

2.3.6 Prediction of the lower 3 dB frequency (f₁)

f_1 is the frequency in low band at which the gain of the amplifier is 3dB down on mid band reference gain (or $\frac{A_M}{\sqrt{2}}$).

$$\text{so,} \quad A_{L(f1)} = \frac{A_M}{\sqrt{2}} = \frac{A_M}{\left[1 + \dfrac{1}{j\,\omega_1\,C_c\,(R_{L1} + R_{in2})}\right]}$$

$$\sqrt{2} = 1 + \frac{1}{j\,\omega_1\,C_c\,(R_{L1} + R_{in2})}$$

$$\sqrt{2} = 1 - j\frac{1}{\omega_1\,C_c\,(R_{L1} + R_{in2})}$$

But, for the magnitude of $1 - jx$ to equal $\sqrt{2}$, x must equal 1.

$$\sqrt{2} = \sqrt{(1^2 + 1^2)}$$

$$\sqrt{2} = \sqrt{1^2 + (\frac{1}{\omega_1 \; C_c \; (R_{L1} + R_{in2})})^2}$$

$$\text{so,} \quad \frac{1}{\omega_1 \; C_c \; (R_{L1} + R_{in2})} = 1$$

$$\text{and,} \quad \omega_1 = \frac{1}{C_c \; (R_{L1} + R_{in2})}$$

$$\boxed{f_1 = \frac{1}{2 \pi \; C_c \; (R_{L1} + R_{in2})}}$$

Example 2.11

Using previous values, i.e. $A_M = 100 \angle 180°$, $R_{L1} = 5\,k\Omega$, $h_{ie2} = 2\,k\Omega$, $R_B = 10\,k\Omega$ and $C_c = 1\,\mu F$, calculate f_1.

$$f_1 = \frac{10^6}{2 \pi \times 1 \times (6.67 \times 10^3)}$$

$f_1 = 23.86\ Hz.$

2.4 Bode plots

A method for showing both gain and phase relationships of a small signal amplifier over a range of frequencies was developed by H.W. Bode and is now referred to as a 'Bode plot'.

Bode plots use logarithmic values for both gain and frequency. As has been explained earlier in this chapter, gains expressed in dB are simply added in order to obtain the overall gain of several cascaded stages. This is also true of Bode plots, which may be added together linearly in order to produce the response for a multi-stage amplifier.

Of course, Bode plots are extremely useful in illustrating any aspect of an amplifier's gain/frequency response, including roll-off, gain peaking, open and closed loop gains, for example as in figure 2.18.

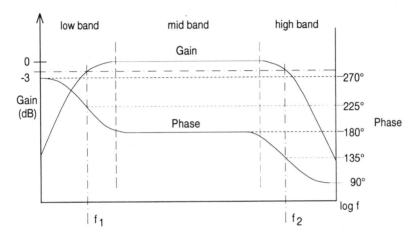

Figure 2.18 *Bode plot for wide band amplifier*

Note that f_1 and f_2 occur when the phase angle (relative to A_M) = 45°, leading for f_1, lagging for f_2.

$$A_H(f_1) = \frac{A_M \angle 180°}{1 - j\,1} = \frac{A_M \angle 180°}{\sqrt{2} \angle -45°} = \frac{A_M}{\sqrt{2}} \angle 225°$$

$$A_H(f_2) = \frac{A_M \angle 180°}{1 + j\,1} = \frac{A_M \angle 180°}{\sqrt{2} \angle 45°} = \frac{A_M}{\sqrt{2}} \angle 135°$$

Another version of the Bode plot is where straight-line approximations are used to represent the response curves. Lines are drawn from the mid band gain level horizontally, and backwards from the linear section of the roll-off curve. The point at which the two lines intersect is the 'break' frequency (3 dB frequency). This method makes the plotting of response curves a much simpler process (as the rate of low and high frequency roll-off is known, i.e. 20 dB / decade or 6 dB per octave).

It can be seen from figure 2.19 that the greatest deviation from the straight-line approximations occur at the 3 dB frequencies in the case of the graph of gain, and either side of those frequencies for the graph of phase. Although no evidence will be offered in this book, it can be proved that the error obtained by the use of straight-line approximations is quite small, i.e. less than 10%.

Clearly, the known errors produced by the use of straight-line approximations can be incorporated into any design procedure, resulting in a much-simplified method of response plotting.

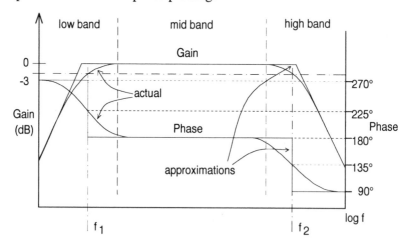

Figure 2.19 *Straight-line approximations*

2.4.1 Phasor representation of gain and phase

Both the amplitude and phase of a signal may be shown by the use of a phasor diagram. If an infinite number of phasors were plotted for an amplifier the tips of the phasors would form the *locus* of the phasor plot.

For a two-stage R-C coupled amplifier, the locus of v_3 (the output voltage) would be a circle, with a diameter of v_3, centred on $A_M/\sqrt{2} \angle 180°$ (as shown in figure 2.20). At 45° each side of v_3 (mid band) would be the −3 dB frequencies, f_1 and f_2.

Note: If an amplifier employed direct coupling then all frequencies from d.c. to mid band would be at a phase angle of 180° and the locus of v_3 would be the high band semi-circle only. Later in this book phasor

plots will be employed to determine the stability, or otherwise, of multi-stage amplifiers with feedback applied to them.

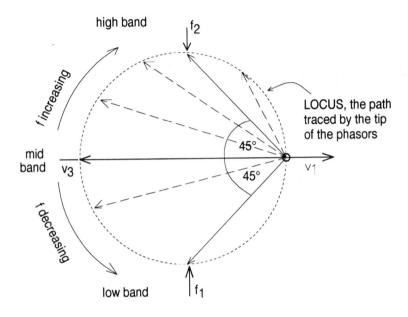

Figure 2.20 *Phasor diagram of gain and phase*

3 Rectangular Waves

The study of rectangular waves is closely linked with that of the frequency response of amplifiers, as the performance of an amplifier can be measured by analysing its response to the application of a step voltage input. In this chapter the parameters of a rectangular wave will be examined, and the relationships between rise time and f_2 and 'sag' and f_1 will be introduced and evaluated.

3.1 Rectangular wave parameters

Figure 3.1 shows a rectangular wave that has the following parameters
- □ amplitude (A)
- □ frequency (period, T)
- □ duty cycle (mark-to-space ratio)
- □ base or reference level.

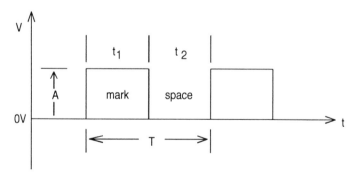

Figure 3.1 *Rectangular wave parameters*

48

Duty Cycle

The duty cycle of a rectangular wave is the ratio of working time (mark) to the total periodic time. It is sometimes quoted as a ratio ($\dfrac{t_1}{t_1+t_2}$ or $\dfrac{t_1}{T}$) or, more commonly, as a percentage

$$\text{duty cycle} = \frac{t_1}{T} \times 100\%.$$

Mark-to-space ratio

This is the ratio of the pulse width, mark (logic 1), to the time interval between pulses, space (logic 0).

Pulse repetition rate (p.r.r.)

This is the periodic time (T).

Pulse recurrence frequency (p.r.f.)

This is the frequency of the waveform ($\dfrac{1}{T}$).

Example 3.1

Calculate duty cycle, mark-to-space ratio, p.r.r. and p.r.f. of the waveform shown in figure 3.2.

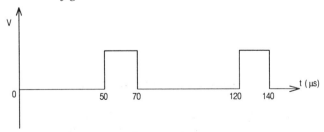

Figure 3.2 *Waveform for example 3.1*

$$duty\ cycle = \frac{t_1}{T} = \frac{20}{70} = 0.286:1 \quad or \quad \underline{28.6\ \%}$$

Mark-to-space ratio: $20:50 = \underline{\mathbf{2:5}}$

P.r.r.: $= \underline{70\ \mu s}$

$$p.r.f. = \frac{1}{T} = \frac{1}{70 \times 10^{-6}} = \frac{10^6}{70} = \underline{\mathbf{14.286\ kHz}}$$

Example 3.2

Draw a 1 kHz pulsed waveform which has a 25% duty cycle.

$$\underline{T = 1\ ms}$$

Mark = 25% x 1 ms $= \underline{250\ \mu s}$

$$\underline{Space = 750\ \mu s}$$

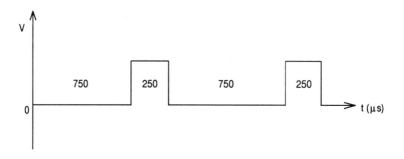

Figure 3.3 *Solution waveform*

It is important to appreciate that there is no such thing as the perfect rectangular wave as this would entail a voltage or current changing from one level to another in zero time. However, it is obvious that any change of level must take a finite time. Consequently, the sides of a rectangular wave can never be vertical and, as illustrated in figure 3.4, the 'corners' are rounded.

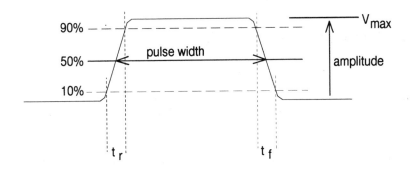

3.4 Practical square wave parameters

The measurement of essential parameters of a practical rectangular wave is made unreliable by the round corners, leading to the use of standard definitions for the rise time, fall time and pulse width of a rectangular wave.

Rise time (t_r)

This is the time taken for the amplitude of the signal to rise from 10% of V_{max} to 90% of V_{max}, measured on the leading edge of the pulse.

Fall time (t_f)

Measured on the trailing edge of the pulse, this is a measure of the time taken for the amplitude to fall from 90% of maximum to 10%.

Pulse width

This is measured at 50% amplitude.

Rectangular waves may be manipulated by applying them to simple R-C circuits. This enables a range of wave shapes to be derived from a rectangular wave.

For example, if a rectangular wave is integrated its rise and fall times will be extended, producing a 'smoothing' effect on the waveform. However, if a rectangular wave is differentiated then the resultant waveform will be that of a pulse, with very short rise and fall times.

3.2 The integrating circuit

The effect of the integrating circuit is controlled by the values of the resistor and capacitor that make up the circuit. The relationship between the 'width' of the applied rectangular wave and the time constant of the integrating circuit determines the shape and amplitude of the resulting output waveform. The circuit and waveforms for the condition where the width of the rectangular pulse is greater than the time constant of the C-R circuit are illustrated in figure 3.5.

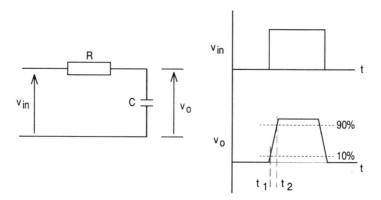

Figure 3.5 *Integrating circuit and waveform*

The rise time of v_0 can be derived mathematically by calculating the time at 90% of V_{max} and subtracting the time at 10% of V_{max}. The time can be calculated with the formula

$$v_0 = V_{max} (1 - e^{(\frac{-t}{CR})})$$

At 10% of V_{max}

$$0.1 \, V_{max} = V_{max} (1 - e^{\frac{-t}{CR}})$$

$$0.1 = 1 - e^{\frac{-t}{CR}}$$

$$e^{\frac{-t}{CR}} = 1 - 0.1 = 0.9$$

$$-\frac{t}{CR} = \log_e 0.9 = -0.1$$

$$t_1 = 0.1\,C\,R$$

At 90% of V_{max}

$$0.9\,V_{max} = V_{max}(1 - e^{\frac{-t}{CR}})$$

$$0.9 = 1 - e^{\frac{-t}{CR}}$$

$$e^{\frac{-t}{CR}} = 1 - 0.9 = 0.1$$

$$-\frac{t}{CR} = \log_e 0.1 = -2.3$$

$$t_2 = 2.3\,C\,R$$

Rise time (t_r)

$$t_r = t_2 - t_1$$

$$t_r = 2.3\,C\,R - 0.1\,C\,R$$

$$\boxed{t_r = 2.2\,C\,R}$$

Integrating circuits can be used to introduce a short time delay. However, the exponential curve of voltage rise across the capacitor is unsuitable for many digital circuits and a Schmitt trigger (or voltage comparator) has to be used to square-up the switching pulse. Figure 3.6 shows the effect of the integrating circuit in combination with the Schmitt trigger producing a short time delay.

Figure 3.6 shows an arrangement in which the C-R integrating circuit causes the voltage across the capacitor to rise exponentially towards the input voltage level. The Schmitt trigger circuit produces a low output until the rising signal applied to its input reaches a preset level. At that point, the output rapidly changes state and goes high. The time delay is determined by the time constant of the C-R circuit.

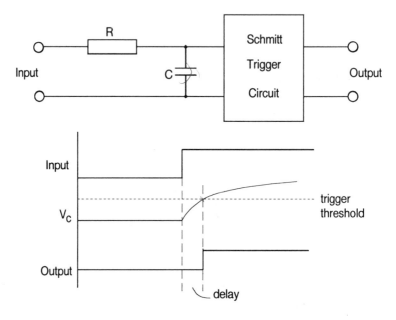

Figure 3.6 *Delay circuit and waveforms*

3.2.1 The link between f₂ and rise time

The rise time of a waveform produced when a step input is applied to a C-R circuit (e.g. the input to a stage of amplification) can be related to the upper cut-off frequency, f_2, of an amplifier.

With reference to figure 3.7, the series C-R circuit is often referred to as a Thévenin's arrangement, and the parallel circuit is known as a Norton's circuit. It is possible to equate the two circuits via Thévenin to Norton transformation, hence the series and parallel circuits are equivalent.

If the two circuits are equivalent then any link between the rise time of the C-R series circuit will apply equally to the C-R parallel circuit.

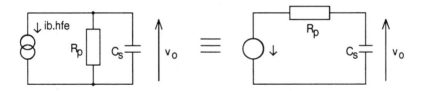

Figure 3.7 *Norton and Thévenin circuits*

From earlier work with cascaded amplifiers, it is known that

$$f_2 = \frac{1}{2 \pi C_s R_p} \quad \dots (1)$$

From work in this chapter it has been shown that

$$t_r = 2.2 \, C \, R$$

rearranging gives

$$C \, R = \frac{t_r}{2.2} \quad \dots (2)$$

If C and R are equated to Cs and Rp and equation (2) is substituted into equation (1)

$$f_2 = \frac{1}{2 \pi \dfrac{t_r}{2.2}}$$

$$f_2 = \frac{2.2}{2 \pi t_r}$$

$$f_2 = \frac{0.35}{t_r}$$

3.3 The differentiating circuit

If the capacitor and resistor in the integrating circuit are transposed, a differentiating circuit is produced. When a rectangular wave is applied to this type of circuit, distortion known as *sag* occurs.

The time constant of the C-R circuit determines the shape of the output waveform. In figure 3.8, the time constant is a little less than the pulse width. If the time constant is greater than the pulse width the output waveform will be more rectangular than shown. If the time constant is smaller than the pulse width it may appear as a short transitory 'spike'.

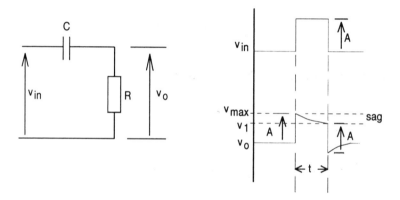

Figure 3.8 *Differentiating circuit and waveform*

The output waveform from a differentiating circuit will vary according to the relationship between the input pulse width and the time constant of the C-R circuit.

3.3.1 Deriving an expression for sag

$$sag = v_{max} - v_1$$

$$v_1 = V_{max}\, e^{\frac{-t}{CR}}$$

$$sag = V_{max} - V_{max}\, e^{\frac{-t}{CR}}$$

$$\text{sag} = V_{max}(1 - e^{\frac{-t}{CR}})$$

$$\% \text{ sag} = \frac{V_{max}(1 - e^{\frac{-t}{CR}})}{V_{max}} \times 100\%$$

$$\boxed{\% \text{ sag} = 100(1 - e^{\frac{-t}{CR}})}$$

Example 3.3

Calculate the value of the capacitance in a differentiating circuit if $R = 1\ k\Omega$ and a 50 Hz rectangular wave is applied. The output must not exhibit more than 5% sag. $t = T/2$, i.e. 10 ms.

$$5 = 100(1 - e^{\frac{-t}{CR}})$$

$$0.05 = 1 - e^{\frac{-t}{CR}}$$

$$e^{\frac{-t}{CR}} = 1 - 0.05$$

$$e^{\frac{-t}{CR}} = 0.95$$

$$\frac{-t}{CR} = log_e\ 0.95$$

rearranging to make C the subject

$$C = \frac{-t}{R\ log_e\ 0.95} = -\frac{10 \times 10^{-3}}{1 \times 10^3 \times log_e\ 0.95}$$

$$\underline{C \approx 195\ \mu F}$$

3.3.2 Linking f_1 with sag

As f_2 was linked with the rise time of a rectangular wave signal, so f_1 can be linked with sag.

Consider the binomial expansion of e^x

$$e^{+x} = 1 + x + \frac{x^2}{2!} + \frac{x^3}{3!} + \frac{x^4}{4!} \ldots \text{ etc.}$$

$$e^{-x} = 1 - x + \frac{x^2}{2!} - \frac{x^3}{3!} + \frac{x^4}{4!} \ldots \text{ etc.}$$

if x is very small . . . .

$$e^{+x} \approx 1 + x$$

$$e^{-x} \approx 1 - x$$

for x, read $\dfrac{-t_1}{CR}$, and t_1 = t at f_1

$$e^{\frac{-t_1}{CR}} \approx 1 - \frac{t_1}{CR}$$

$$\text{so sag} \approx 1 - \left(1 - \frac{t_1}{CR} \right)$$

$$\text{sag} \approx \frac{t_1}{CR}$$

$$\% \text{ sag} \approx \frac{t_1}{CR} \times 100\%$$

Equating the expression for '% sag' to the cascaded amplifier in chapter 2

$$f_1 = \frac{1}{2\pi\, C_c\, (R_{L1} + R_{in2})}$$

$$\text{sag} = \frac{t_1}{C_c\, (R_{L1} + R_{in2})}$$

substitute for $C_c (R_{L1} + R_{in2}) = \dfrac{t_1}{sag}$ into $f_1 = \dfrac{1}{2 \pi C_c (R_{L1} + R_{in2})}$

$$f_1 = \frac{1 \times sag\%}{2 \pi t_1 \times 100}$$

but $t_1 = \dfrac{t_p}{2} = \dfrac{1}{2f}$

$$f_1 = \frac{sag\% \times 2f}{2 \pi \times 100}$$ and $$sag\% = \frac{f_1 \pi \times 100\%}{f}$$

4 Multiple Transistor Circuits

In this chapter a number of multiple transistor circuits will be examined and analysed. Each of these circuits can be deployed in more complex applications, for example, stabilised power supplies, power amplifiers and operational amplifiers.

4.1 The difference amplifier

The difference amplifier, or 'long-tailed pair', is often used as the input stage of operational amplifiers, comparators and ECL (Emitter-Coupled Logic) gates. The circuit is especially useful when d.c. or very low frequencies are to be amplified as it has many advantages over a conventional common-emitter amplifier.

The circuit has two independent inputs making it possible to operate in two modes, 'common mode' and 'difference (or differential) mode'. When operating in common mode we are interested in how the circuit reacts to identical signals applied at the inputs, for example noise, power supply hum or changes in bias due to temperature-induced drift. In difference mode it is the difference between the two inputs that is processed. The ideal difference amplifier will have a common mode gain of zero, the differential mode gain being a function of component values and transistor parameters. Of course, the practical amplifier is not ideal and will have some common mode gain. However, this is likely to be very small compared with the differential-mode gain.

The ratio of common-mode gain, A_{CM}, to differential-mode gain, A_{DM}, is a measure of the circuit's ability to reject the unwanted common-mode signals. This is called the Common Mode Rejection Ratio (CMRR) and it is expressed as a logarithmic ratio

$$CMRR = 20 \log_{10} \frac{A_{DM}}{A_{CM}} \; dB$$

Figure 4.1 shows the basic circuit arrangement for a difference amplifier.

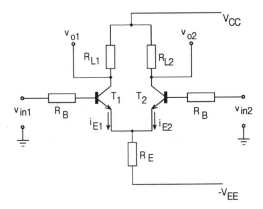

Figure 4.1 *Basic difference amplifier circuit*

Note that there are 2 inputs, vin1 and vin2, and 2 outputs, vo1 and vo2.

In terms of input signals, the circuit can amplify the difference between two signals applied at the inputs or can act as a single-ended amplifier, with one input connected to ground. In addition, outputs can be taken between either of the output terminals and ground or across the two terminals.

The circuit resembles a pair of simple common-emitter amplifiers with a shared emitter resistor and no emitter bypass capacitor. This would appear to produce a degree of negative feedback and, as a consequence, an amplifier with rather poor gain. However, the action of the second transistor does away with the need for emitter decoupling. Consider the following scenario. Suppose that a signal is applied to T_1 base with T_2 base held constant so that T_2 is conducting, i.e. the amplifier is operated in single-ended input mode. As the applied signal goes positive T_1 base current increases, its collector current rises and V_C falls. The voltage across the emitter resistor, R_E, tries to rise as more current flows through it. However, the base-emitter voltage of T_2 falls as a result, causing a fall in T_2 emitter current and a reduction in the current in R_E, thereby resisting the initial increase in current in R_E.

Analysis of the circuit can be conducted under the assumption that the device is manufactured on a silicon chip and, therefore, that both transistors will have identical parameters. Under those conditions the circuit will be symmetrical. The differential-mode input voltage, v_{dm}, is the difference between the two input signals

$$v_{dm} = v_{in1} - v_{in2}$$

The common-mode input voltage, v_{cm}, is the average of the two input signals

$$v_{cm} = \frac{v_{in1} + v_{in2}}{2}$$

Each of the input voltages may then be expressed in terms of common-mode input voltage and differential-mode input voltage as follows

$$v_{in1} = v_{cm} - \frac{v_{dm}}{2}$$

$$v_{in2} = v_{cm} + \frac{v_{dm}}{2}$$

The output voltage of either side of the amplifier with respect to ground is the sum of the differential-mode output voltage and the common-mode output voltage, i.e.

$$v_o = v_{dm} A_{DM} + v_{cm} A_{CM}$$

For an ideal amplifier the common mode gain, A_{CM}, is zero and the expression reduces to

$$v_o = v_{dm} A_{DM}$$

The common mode gain is determined by the values of R_L and R_E, such that

$$A_{CM} = K \frac{R_L}{R_E}$$

Clearly, for a low value of common mode gain and a relatively small value for R_L, the value of R_E must be high. To keep the emitter potential at a suitable level for base-emitter biasing, the negative supply, $-V_{EE}$, is used.

The differential-mode gain, A_{DM}, can be expressed as a function of the mutual conductance, g_m, of the transistor, such that, for differential input and differential output

$$A_{DM} = g_m R_L$$

and, for differential input and single-ended output

$$A_{DM} = 0.5 \, g_m R_L$$

Note that $g_m = h_f / h_i$.

Example 4.1

An ideal difference amplifier has the following component values and transistor parameters: h_{ie}: 2 kΩ h_{fe}: 100 $R_L = 5$ kΩ.
If $v_{in1} = +10$ mV and vin2 = −10 mV, calculate the differential mode gain for a single-ended output.

Method 1 (Using $v_o = h_{fe} \, i_b \, R_L$)

$$i_b = \frac{v_b}{h_{ie}} = \frac{10 \times 10^{-3}}{2 \times 10^3} = 5 \times 10^{-6} \, A$$

$$i_b = 5 \, \mu A$$

$$v_o = h_{fe} \, i_b \, R_L = 100 \times 5 \times 10^{-6} \times 5 \times 10^3$$

$$v_o = 2.5 \, V$$

$$A_{DM} = \frac{v_o}{v_{dm}} = \frac{2.5}{(10 - -10) \times 10^{-3}}$$

$$A_{DM} = \frac{2500}{20} = \underline{125}$$

Method 2 (using $A_{DM} = 0.5 \, g_m \, R_L$)

$$g_m = \frac{h_{fe}}{h_{ie}} = \frac{100}{2000} = 0.05$$

$$A_{DM} = 0.5 \, g_m \, R_L = 0.5 \times 0.05 \times 5 \times 10^3$$

$$A_{DM} = \underline{125}$$

There are various enhancements to the basic difference amplifier, all designed to improve performance or stability.

4.1.1 Active or constant-current tail

As indicated earlier, the common-mode gain is determined, in part, by the value of R_E. The larger the value of R_E, the lower the common-mode gain. However, a very large resistance would require a large bias voltage $-V_{EE}$, which is impractical.

A popular solution to this problem is to employ a constant-current generator, e.g. a bi-polar transistor, in place of the emitter resistor, as illustrated in figure 4.2.

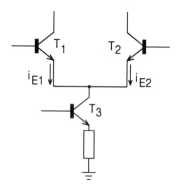

Figure 4.2 *Constant-current tail*

This provides an effective high resistance, in the order of $M\Omega$, whilst not demanding any special power supply requirements.

If a difference amplifier has been constructed using discrete components there is a strong possibility that the two halves of the amplifier will not be perfectly balanced. In this case additional components will be required to provide some manual adjustment of circuit balance. These components, usually a preset potentiometer, can be inserted into the collector or emitter circuits of the transistors. Adjustment of the potentiometer can then be carried out in order to ensure that equal current flows in each transistor.

Figures 4.3 and 4.4 show collector and emitter balancing circuits respectively. Note that to balance dissimilar transistors $R_1 \neq R_2$.

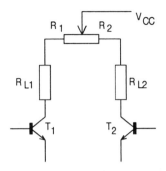

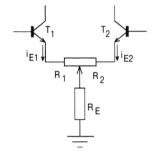

Figure 4.3 *Collector balancing circuit*   **Figure 4.4** *Emitter balancing circuit*

More complex enhancements can be achieved by combining multiple-transistor circuits, some of which will be introduced later in this chapter.

The advantages of the long-tailed pair are as follows

- □ good thermal stability
- □ very low common-mode drift
- □ no d.c. content at the differential outputs
- □ greater gain than a single-ended amplifier

Many modern operational amplifiers require very high input impedances and employ field effect transistors in the difference amplifiers. Input impedances in the order of 10^{12} Ω are achieved using these circuits.

4.2 The Darlington amplifier

There are instances when a circuit designer requires a stage of amplification with large current gain and very high input impedance. A configuration that provides these conditions is the compound amplifier or Darlington amplifier (other names for this circuit are Darlington pair or super-alpha pair). The high current gain of this arrangement is achieved by driving the base of a second transistor directly with the output current of the first transistor. Figure 4.5 shows the basic arrangement for a Darlington amplifier connected as an emitter follower. The overall current gain of the pair is I_o / I_{in}.

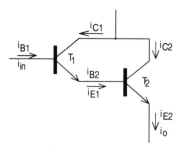

Figure 4.5 *Basic Darlington amplifier*

4.2.1 Derivation of overall current gain (emitter follower)

Let the forward current gain of T_1 be h_{FE1} and for T_2, h_{FE2}, then

$$i_{E1} = i_{B1} + i_{B1} h_{FE1}$$

$$i_{E1} = i_{B1} (1 + h_{FE1})$$

$$i_{E2} = i_{B2} + i_{B2} h_{FE2}$$

$$i_{E2} = i_{B2} (1 + h_{FE2})$$

but $i_{B2} = i_{E1}$, therefore, substituting $i_{E1} = i_{B1} (1 + h_{FE1})$ for I_{B2}

$$i_{E2} = i_{B1} (1 + h_{FE1}) (1 + h_{FE2})$$

$$h_{FE(eff)} = \frac{i_o}{i_{in}} = \frac{i_{E2}}{i_{B1}} = (1 + h_{FE1}) (1 + h_{FE2})$$

In the case of the emitter follower, the load resistance is connected in the emitter circuit of the Darlington pair. Another arrangement of the same configuration would place the load resistance in the collector. In this circuit the output current of the amplifier would be the total collector currents of the two transistors and the derivation of the expression for overall current gain would be slightly different, see figure 4.6.

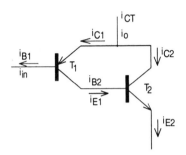

Figure 4.6 **Darlington pair as a c-e amplifier**

4.2.2 Derivation of overall current gain (common-emitter amplifier)

$$I_{CT} = I_{C1} + I_{C2}$$

$$I_{C1} = I_{B1} h_{FE1}$$

$$i_{C2} = I_{B2} h_{FE2}$$

but $i_{B2} = i_{E1} = i_{B1} + i_{B1} h_{FE1}$, therefore substituting

$$i_{C2} = (i_{B1} + i_{B1} h_{FE1}) h_{FE2}$$

$$i_{C2} = i_{B1} (1 + h_{FE1}) h_{FE2}$$

$$i_{CT} = i_{C1} + i_{C2} = i_{B1} h_{FE1} + i_{B1} (1 + h_{FE1}) h_{FE2}$$

dividing by i_{B1}

$$\frac{I_{CT}}{i_{B1}} = h_{FE1} + (1 + h_{FE1}) h_{FE2}$$

and multiplying out the brackets gives

$$h_{FE(eff)} = \frac{i_o}{i_{in}} = \frac{i_{CT}}{i_{B1}} = h_{FE1} + h_{FE2} + h_{FE1} h_{FE2}$$

Example 4.2

Compare the overall current gain for emitter follower and common emitter configurations when T_1 has a forward current gain of 100 and T_2 has a forward current gain of 20.

a) Emitter follower

$$\text{Overall current gain} = (1 + h_{FE1})(1 + h_{FE2})$$

$$h_{FE(eff)} = (1 + 100)(1 + 20)$$

$$\underline{\mathbf{h_{FE(eff)} = 2121}}$$

b) Common emitter

$$h_{FE(eff)} = h_{FE1} + h_{FE2} + h_{FE1}\, h_{FE2}$$

$$h_{FE(eff)} = 100 + 20 + (100 \times 20)$$

$$\underline{\mathbf{h_{FE(eff)} = 2120}}$$

Compound transistors are used in many applications, for example

- op-amps (in the difference amplifier)
- complementary push-pull output stages
- stabilised power supplies

where their high current gain and high input impedance are invaluable.

In addition to the NPN arrangements discussed, there is a need, for example in a complementary push-pull output stage, for a compound transistor that performs a PNP action. Consider the circuit in figure 4.7.

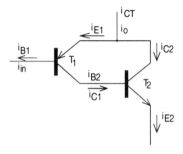

Figure 4.7 *Compound transistor with PNP action*

4.2.3 Derivation of overall current gain (PNP action)

The derivation for this circuit is similar to that of the NPN-input emitter follower except that the current gain of T_1 is simply $I_{B1} \, h_{FE1}$ as it is the collector current of T_1 that drives the base of T_2. Hence

$$i_{C1} = i_{B1} \, h_{FE1}$$

$$i_{E2} = i_{B2} + i_{B2} \, h_{FE2}$$

$$i_{E2} = i_{B2} \, (1 + h_{FE2})$$

but $i_{B2} = i_{B1} \, h_{FE1}$, therefore

$$i_{E2} = i_{B1} \, h_{FE1} \, (1 + h_{FE2})$$

$$\frac{i_{E2}}{i_{B1}} = h_{FE1} \, (1 + h_{FE2})$$

$$h_{FE(eff)} = \frac{i_o}{i_{in}} = \frac{i_{E2}}{i_{B1}} = h_{FE1} + h_{FE1} \, h_{FE2}$$

4.2.4 Input impedance of Darlington amplifier

As indicated earlier in this chapter, one advantage of the compound amplifier is the increase obtained in input impedance. The effective input impedance becomes

$$h_{IE(eff)} = h_{IE1} + h_{IE2} \, (1 + h_{FE1})$$

The compound amplifier is available in a single package, known as a Darlington transistor. Examples include

Motorola	2N6040	(PNP)
Motorola	2N6043	(NPN)
Texas Instruments	BDW53	(NPN)
Texas Instruments	BDW54	(PNP)

4.3 The cascode amplifier

Another multiple transistor circuit is the cascode amplifier, in which a common-emitter amplifier is directly coupled into a transistor arranged in common-base configuration. This amplifier is frequently employed in integrated circuit amplifiers because of the following features

    ☐   good stability at high frequencies
    ☐   wide bandwidth
    ☐   d.c. level shifting possible
    ☐   can operate as a constant current source

In addition, the cascode arrangement may be applied to circuits already discussed, for example the long-tailed pair (difference amplifier). Figure 4.8 shows the cascode amplifier without biasing components.

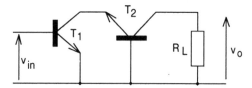

Figure 4.8 *Cascode amplifier*

The voltage gain of the common-emitter stage is kept very low in order to keep to a minimum the Miller effect (the effect of internal base-collector capacitance of the common-emitter configuration at high operating frequencies). The common-base amplifier has voltage gain but no signal inversion and, as a result, no Miller effect is present. The performance of the circuit at high frequencies is, therefore, superior to that of the common-emitter amplifier and it follows that the bandwidth is also greater. The output impedance of the common-base connection is considerably higher than the common-emitter configuration and, as the cascode circuit as a whole has current amplification, it can be used as a high-impedance constant-current generator.

A very common requirement for circuit design is to change the d.c. level upon which a signal is 'sitting'. For example, the removal of the d.c. content of a signal is necessary if the a.c. signal is required to vary about 0 volts. It is possible, of course, to achieve this objective with passive components only. However, such a circuit would produce an attenuation of the a.c. signal.

The use of the cascode amplifier allows a wide range of d.c. 'offsets' to be produced by the adjustment of the d.c. operating conditions of the transistors, that is, by adjusting a preset potientiometer.

4.4 Improving amplifier gain

The gain of any of these amplifiers can be increased by the use of active loads, an example of which is illustrated in figure 4.9.

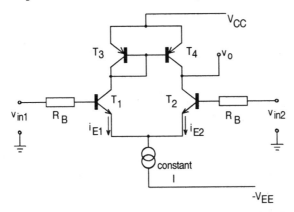

Figure 4.9 *Difference amplifier with active load*

These are constant current sources, e.g. transistors, used in place of resistive loads, providing very high resistance and very low d.c. voltage drop. The disadvantage of using active loads is that the increase in gain that results produces a corresponding fall in bandwidth (from the assumption that the gain-bandwidth product is a constant).

4.5 Combining circuits to enhance performance

It is possible to combine the circuits described in this chapter in order to produce an amplifier whose performance is enhanced when compared with the basic circuit arrangement. For example, the difference amplifier can be designed with Darlington pairs in each half of the amplifier, increasing the current gain and input impedance of the amplifier further, see figure 4.10.

The difference amplifier can also utilise cascode amplifiers, improving its performance at high frequencies.

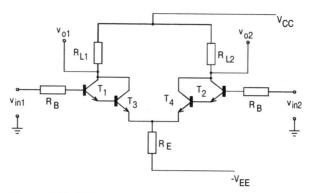

Figure 4.10 *Difference amplifier with Darlington pairs*

4.6 The operational amplifier

The circuits described in this chapter can be used to construct a basic operational amplifier. One of the most popular op-amps is the 741, manufactured by a number of companies, including Philips, National Semiconductor, Texas Instruments and Fairchild.

Although all versions of the 741 are compatible, various improvements in circuit design have been introduced by manufacturers. A typical design is illustrated in figure 4.11.

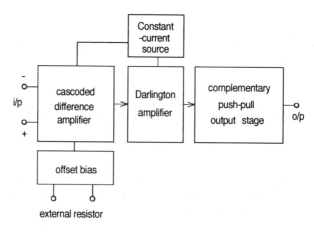

Figure 4.11 Block diagram of 741 op-amp

The difference amplifier used at the inputs of the 741 employs cascoded amplifiers with active loads. The single-ended output is applied to a Darlington amplifier which, in turn, drives a complementary (PNP-NPN) class AB output stage.

Offset bias is applied externally to pins 1 and 5 and frequency compensation is provided internally with a 30 pF capacitor.

Data sheets for the 741 are included in Appendix B.

The 741 is not state-of-the-art so far as op-amp design goes, but is a general-purpose device that is still an industry standard. Its uses are widespread, including

- □ linear amplifiers
- □ voltage comparators
- □ active filters
- □ integrators and differentiators

A subset of its specifications is presented in table 4.1.

Table 4.1 *Typical values for 741 parameters*

Parameter	Typical value
input resistance	2 MΩ
large-signal voltage gain	106 dB
output voltage swing	±14 V ($R_L = 10$ kΩ)
common-mode rejection ratio	90 dB
bandwidth	10^6
slew rate	0.5 V / μs
supply current	1.7 mA
power consumption	50 mW

Note: The slew rate of an op-amp is the maximum rate of change of output voltage that the amplifier can achieve. It is usually quoted in Volts per microsecond.

5 Operational Amplifiers

Chapter 4 introduced the concept of the operational amplifier, a high-gain multi-stage linear amplifier. The op-amp can be operated under 'open-loop' conditions, that is to say with no feedback applied, when it will exhibit high voltage gain, but rather a narrow bandwidth. However, it is much more likely to be operated with considerable amounts of negative feedback applied. The gain is reduced, of course, but the bandwidth is increased by a similar amount (the gain/bandwidth product of an op-amp is a constant).

The name 'operational amplifier' is derived from its use for carrying out linear operations such as signal addition, differentiation and integration. These operations are employed, amongst other things, in the design and construction of analogue computers.

In this chapter some introductory work on operational amplifiers will be undertaken, beginning with ideal amplifier characteristics and progressing to the basic amplifier configurations and their gain, frequency response and input and output impedances. After that earlier level revision, various areas of amplifier operation and design will be considered, including slew rate limiting and common mode rejection ratio (CMRR). The work done in this chapter will prepare the reader for chapter 6, in which applications of op-amps will be considered.

There are three types of operational amplifier commonly available

- □ single-ended input/single-ended output
- □ differential input/single-ended output
- □ differential input/differential output

Single-ended inputs and outputs are considered relative to ground, although this does not have to be shown on the circuit diagram. Differential inputs and outputs have no relationship with ground and are described as 'floating' or 'earth-free'. They only have a relationship with ground when connected externally. In a differential arrangement it is the difference between the signals at the two terminals (inputs or outputs) that is of any consequence.

An input may be classed as inverting or non-inverting, depending upon the phase relationship between the output signal and the applied signal. By convention, a '−' sign indicates an inverting input terminal and a '+' sign indicates a non-inverting terminal.

Figure 5.1 illustrates the conventional circuit symbols for the three varieties identified above. Figure 5.1 (a) illustrates an inverting single-ended input/single-ended output op-amp, (b) shows the more popular differential input/single-ended output arrangement and (c) illustrates the differential input/differential output amplifier.

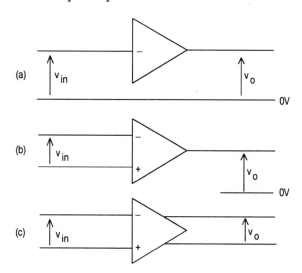

Figure 5.1 Operational amplifier types

The operational amplifier has internal resistances across the input terminals and from the output terminal to ground. In a practical op-amp these resistances have real values, the input resistance R_i is very high and the output resistance R_o is very small. However, for most op-amp applications it is the external components that determine the operating parameters of the circuit and the internal resistances of the op-amp may be considered 'ideal' and, as a result, negligible.

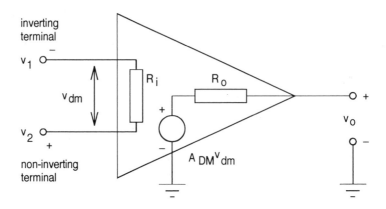

Figure 5.2 *Op-amp equivalent circuit*

Figure 5.2 shows the equivalent circuit for an operational amplifier. The two input terminals have input voltages, v_1 and v_2, applied to them, the difference between the two voltages being v_{dm}. The differential-mode gain A_{DM} operates on the differential input voltage to produce the output voltage v_o. The internal input resistance R_i is very high, possibly in the order of $10^6\,\Omega$. The output resistance of the op-amp, Ro, is very low, typically less than $100\,\Omega$.

In a practical operational amplifier the input terminals are considered to have virtually no voltage across them due to their extremely high gain and limited output voltage, e.g. ± 12 V. With the high input resistance the current flowing in the terminals would be extremely low, for example if $R_i = 10^6\,\Omega$ and $v_d = 10\,\mu$V, the current would be

$$i_d = \frac{V_d}{R_i} = \frac{10 \times 10^{-6}}{10^6} = \textbf{10 pA}$$

The values of these parameters in modern operational amplifiers are dependent upon the technology employed in the op-amp design. For example, some op-amps use JFET input devices and have input impedances in the region of 1012 W or more. Of course, all of this information is available from manufacturers' data sheets, examples of which appear in Appendix B.

5.1 Ideal op-amp characteristics

At this level of study, an operational amplifier is considered to have what are described as 'ideal' characteristics in order to simplify analysis. Of course, it can be proved that these are only approximations of actual amplifier characteristics and small errors occur as a result of their use. However, these errors can be considered negligible for our purposes.

Table 5.1 shows each of the main amplifier characteristics and its 'ideal' value.

Table 5.1 *Ideal op-amp characteristics*

Characteristic	'Ideal' value
Open loop gain	∞
Input impedance	$\infty \, \Omega$
Bandwidth	∞
Output impedance	$0 \, \Omega$
Input I and V	0

Note that the input voltage and current are called 'offsets' and should ideally be zero. In practical op-amps a very small amount of current (in the order of pA in modern designs) will be flowing in the input terminals in order to obtain zero output voltage.

5.2 Amplifier configurations

Of the three types of operational amplifier illustrated in figure 5.1, by far the most popular, and that employed by all op-amp circuits described in this book, is the differential-input/single-ended output arrangement. The use of differential inputs allows for much greater flexibility in amplifier design, with many applications available from a single type of op-amp.

Operational amplifiers are employed to perform a wide range of tasks, including amplifiers, waveform generators and filters. For all of these applications the op-amp will be connected in one of two basic configurations, as an inverting or non-inverting amplifier. The two types differ in the manner in which negative feedback from the output is applied to the input. In the inverting amplifier feedback is applied in shunt with the input signal, whereas in the non-inverting amplifier, feedback is applied in series with the input. These two main configurations will now be considered and analysed.

5.2.1 The inverting amplifier

The input to this amplifier is connected to the inverting input terminal. The non-inverting input must be connected directly, or indirectly, to ground. Feedback from the output, negative owing to the inverting action of the amplifier, is connected to the non-inverting input. This connection means that the feedback voltage is in shunt with the input signal. The circuit arrangement for an inverting amplifier is shown in figure 5.3.

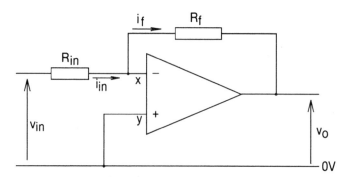

Figure 5.3 *Inverting amplifier*

If we assume that no current will flow into the terminals of the op-amp then it follows that any current flowing in R_{in}, i.e. i_{in}, will also flow in R_f. Therefore i_f equals i_{in}.

If point x is assumed to be at 0 volts, then as $i_{in} = i_f$

$$\frac{V_{in}}{R_{in}} = \frac{-V_o}{R_f}$$

and voltage gain Av $= \dfrac{V_o}{V_{in}} = \boxed{-\dfrac{R_f}{R_{in}}}$

Note that the – sign indicates an inversion of v_o relative to v_{in}.

Input impedance

If the voltage between the two input terminals is treated as zero (an ideal op-amp), then the resistance between those terminals must also be treated as zero.

Therefore, the input resistance of the amplifier is equal to that of the input resistor R_{in}, i.e. $Z_{in} = R_{in}$.

Note: The application of negative feedback in shunt with the input of the amplifier tends to reduce the overall input impedance. However, the effect is a function of amplifier voltage gain such that the greater the gain the smaller the effect. In most applications the effect is so small as to be negligible.

Output impedance

Ideally, the output impedance, Z_o, of an operational amplifier is considered to be 0 Ω. In practice, however, it is in the order of a few ohms. Given this assumption, the load placed on the output of an op-amp may be **any value**, and the output voltage will be unaffected (subject to the ability of the op-amp to deliver the current for that load).

Because the op-amp has a very high input impedance and a very low output impedance it may be referred to as a *buffer amplifier*.

5.2.2 Non-inverting amplifier

As its name suggests, this amplifier does not invert the applied signal. The signal is applied to the non-inverting terminal with feedback being applied to the inverting terminal. The input resistor R_{in} is connected from the inverting terminal to ground, as illustrated in figure 5.4. The negative feedback applied in the non-inverting amplifier is applied in series with the input resistance, producing a higher overall input impedance for this amplifier than the equivalent inverting amplifier. The gain of the non-inverting amplifier is determined in similar fashion to that of the inverting amplifier.

Again, assuming that $i_{in} = i_f$

$$\frac{V_{in}}{R_{in}} = \frac{V_o}{R_f + R_{in}}$$

$$\frac{V_o}{V_{in}} = \frac{R_f + R_{in}}{R_{in}}$$

$$A_v = \frac{V_o}{V_{in}} = \frac{R_f}{R_{in}} + \frac{R_{in}}{R_{in}}$$

$$A_v = 1 + \frac{R_f}{R_{in}}$$

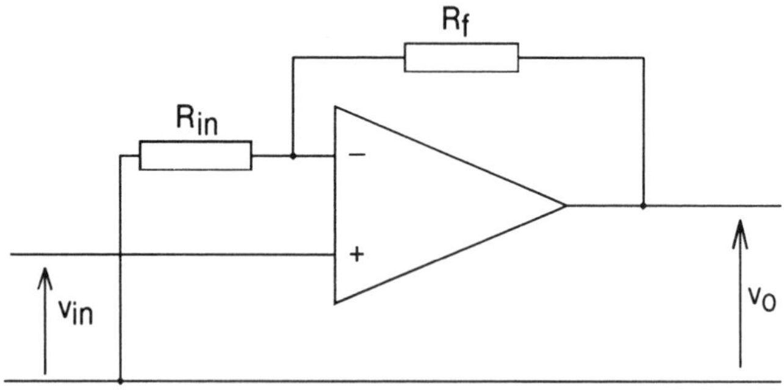

Figure 5.4 *Non-inverting amplifier*

Input impedance

The input impedance of the non-inverting amplifier, as already suggested, is higher than the inverting amplifier and is in the order of several MΩ.

Output impedance

As with the inverting amplifier, the output impedance is very low and may be treated as zero Ω in most applications. Consider the effects of increasing the value of R_{in} towards infinity. The gain of the non-inverting amplifier will tend towards unity as the R_f / R_{in} part of the expression becomes smaller, tending towards zero. The effect of this action is to produce a voltage follower, i.e. a device with an extremely high input impedance, a very low output impedance and a gain of unity.

$$A_v = 1 + \frac{R_f}{R_{in}} = 1 + \frac{R_f}{\infty}$$

$$A_v = 1 + 0 = 1$$

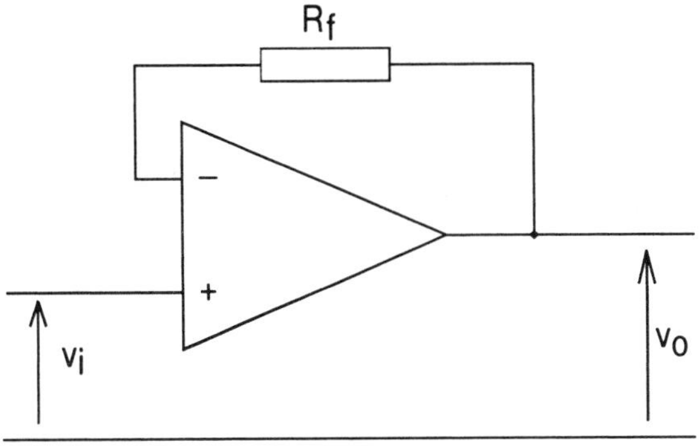

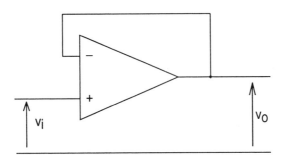

Figure 5.5 *Voltage follower*

As R_f has no effect on the gain of the amplifier, it may be any value, even a short-circuit, see figure 5.6.

Figure 5.6 *With R_f short-circuit*

This is the perfect buffer or voltage follower, with a gain of 1, an input impedance of several $M\Omega$ and an output impedance approximating to zero.

5.3 Frequency response of an op-amp

For any operational amplifier, the product of gain and bandwidth is a **constant**. If the amplifier is operated under 'open-loop' conditions its gain will be very high but its bandwidth will be quite narrow. If negative feedback is applied the gain will be reduced and the bandwidth will be increased, see figure 5.7.

For a typical, if rather old, op-amp, the 741, the gain/bandwidth product is approximately 10^6.

It can be shown that the 'roll-off' rate (the slope of the falling edge of the response curve) of a 741 is 20 dB per decade.

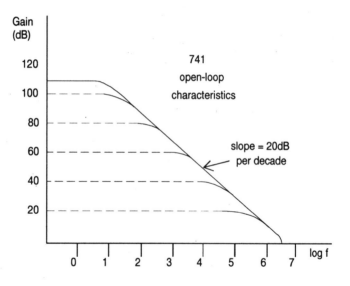

Figure 5.7 *741 open-loop frequency response*

5.4 Slew rate limiting

The 'slew rate' of an operational amplifier is the maximum rate of change of voltage achievable at its output. When a combination of high signal amplitude and high frequency occurs, 'slew-rate limiting' may take place, causing the output signal to be distorted.

For a 741 the slew rate is 500,000 volts per second. This may sound high but is now considered very low when compared with the slew rate of modern op-amps. It may be beneficial to consider the change over a period of 1 μs - in the case of the 741 it is 0.5 V/μs.

Consider a situation where the expected output of a 741 is a rectangular wave with an amplitude of ± 10v and a frequency of 100 kHz. The expected output signal should be approximately rectangular. However, the output of the 741 would change by only 2.5 V in the 5 μs before it began to fall. The actual output waveform would be triangular, as illustrated in figure 5.8.

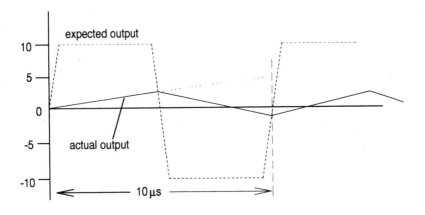

Figure 5.8 *The effect of slew rate limiting*

The output is plotted over a given time period to establish the slope of the output waveform. In this example the output would have reached the 5 volt level after 10 μs (for the given rate of change of 0.5 V / μs). However, the output never gets to that level as the expected output signal begins to fall. The fall of output takes place at the same rate as the rise, causing the output to be triangular in shape.

The effect of slew rate on a rectangular wave signal is simply explained. If the rate of change of voltage on the rising and/or falling edges of the waveform is higher than the slew rate of the op-amp, then slew rate limiting will take place and the resultant slope will be that of the slew rate of the op-amp.

5.4.1 Predicting the effect of slew rate on a sine wave

When the signal being processed by the operational amplifier is a sine wave, the effect of slew rate is less easy to predict. In order to determine whether the output waveform will be distorted by a particular op-amp, the maximum rate of change of the applied sine wave must be known. If this is higher than the slew rate of the op-amp, distortion will occur.

The instantaneous voltage at any point on a sine wave is determined by the expression $v = V_{max} \sin \omega t$. The rate of change of v is the differential of v with time, i.e. dv / dt.

$$\frac{dv}{dt} = V_{max}\, \omega \cos \omega t$$

The maximum rate of change occurs when the sine wave passes through zero, that is when its amplitude is zero volts. This is true when, for example, $t = 0$, and this is a convenient point to use. At $t = 0$, $\omega t = 0$ and therefore

$$\frac{dv}{dt} = V_{max}\, \omega \cos 0$$

As $\cos 0 = 1$

$$\boxed{\frac{dv}{dt} = V_{max}\, \omega}$$

or the maximum rate of change of voltage equals the peak amplitude multiplied by the frequency.

Example 5.1

The output signal of a 741 op-amp is a sine wave of 10 volts peak at a frequency of 1 kHz. Does the signal suffer slew-rate distortion?

$$\frac{dv}{dt} \, max \; = \; 10 \times 2\,\pi \times 1000$$

$$\frac{dv}{dt} \, max \; = \; \underline{\textbf{62,831 volts/second}}$$

So the output would NOT suffer slew-rate distortion since this rate is less than the 500,000 V/s slew rate of the 741.

Example 5.2

The output voltage of an op-amp should be 10 volts peak at a frequency of 20 kHz. Does slew rate limiting occur?

$$\frac{dv}{dt} \, max \; = \; 10 \times 20 \times 10^3 \times 2\,\pi$$

$$\frac{dv}{dt} \, max \; = \; \underline{\textbf{1.256} \times \textbf{10}^6 \textbf{ volts/second}}$$

Slew-rate limiting of the output signal WILL occur in this case.

5.5 The differential amplifier

In chapter 4 the differential (or difference) amplifier was examined in discrete component form. The operational amplifier equivalent of that circuit, with a differential input and single-ended output, will now be analysed. The uses of the amplifier stem from its ability to amplify the difference between the two signals (neither of which is at ground potential) at its inputs, whilst providing a high degree of rejection of signals common to both inputs. A typical example is illustrated in figure 5.9 where the difference between the voltage at point A and that at point B is required. Any signals such as hum or noise common to both points must be severely attenuated. The diagram shows that the two points are connected, via equal-value series resistors (R_{in}), to the two inputs of the op-amp. Two equal-value resistors (R_f) are employed to provide negative feedback. As with the discrete component amplifier, this circuit has a differential-mode voltage gain, A_{DM}, and a common-mode voltage gain, A_{CM}. The ratio of A_{DM} to A_{CM} is the common mode rejection ratio (CMRR).

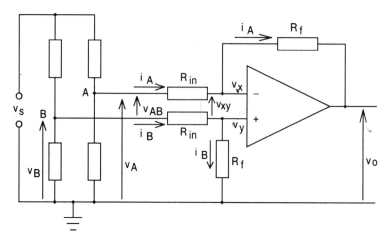

Figure 5.9 Differential amplifier

For analysis the op-amp is assumed to have ideal characteristics, so it can be assumed that the voltage between the two input terminals, v_{xy}, is zero and that no current is flowing in the input terminals. So

$$i_A = \frac{v_A - v_x}{R_{in}}$$

Also

$$i_A = \frac{v_x - v_o}{R_f}$$

$$\frac{v_A - v_x}{R_{in}} = \frac{v_x - v_o}{R_f}$$

separating the terms on each side of the equation gives

$$\frac{v_A}{R_{in}} - \frac{v_x}{R_{in}} = \frac{v_x}{R_f} - \frac{v_o}{R_f}$$

$$\frac{v_A}{R_{in}} + \frac{v_o}{R_f} = \frac{v_x}{R_f} + \frac{v_x}{R_{in}}$$

$$\frac{v_A}{R_{in}} + \frac{v_o}{R_f} = v_x \left(\frac{1}{R_f} + \frac{1}{R_{in}} \right)$$

multiply both sides by $R_f.R_{in}$

$$v_A R_f + v_o R_{in} = v_x (R_f + R_{in})$$

$$\frac{v_A R_f + v_o R_{in}}{R_f + R_{in}} = v_x \quad \ldots \ldots (1)$$

$$i_B = \frac{v_B}{R_{in} + R_f}$$

$$v_y = i_B R_f = \frac{v_B R_f}{R_{in} + R_f} \quad \ldots \ldots (2)$$

But $v_{xy} = 0$, therefore $v_x = v_y$, and

$$\frac{v_A R_f + v_o R_{in}}{R_{in} + R_f} = \frac{v_B R_f}{R_{in} + R_f}$$

multiply both sides by $R_{in} + R_f$

$$v_A R_f + v_o R_{in} = v_B R_f$$

rearranging

$$v_o R_{in} = v_B R_f - v_A R_f$$

$$v_o = \frac{R_f (v_B - v_A)}{R_{in}}$$

If $v_{AB} = v_A - v_B$ then $v_B - v_A = -v_{AB}$

$$v_o = \frac{R_f - V_{AB}}{R_{in}}$$

$$\frac{v_o}{-v_{AB}} = \frac{R_f}{R_{in}}$$

$$A_{DM} \text{ (Differential Mode Gain)} = \frac{v_o}{v_{AB}} = -\frac{R_f}{R_{in}}$$

The common mode voltage gain is not, generally, determined from component values but rather by use of manufacturers' data. The differential mode gain can be calculated as shown, the common mode rejection ratio is quoted by the manufacturers of the op-amp and the common mode gain is related to the two other quantities by $A_{CM} = \dfrac{A_{DM}}{CMRR}$. Measurement of common mode gain can be performed with the two inputs connected together as illustrated in figure 5.10.

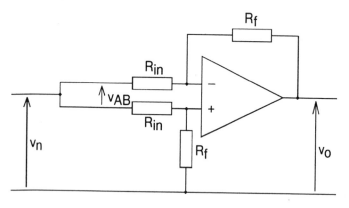

Figure 5.10 *Common mode test arrangement*

If the common mode input voltage is called v_n then $A_{CM} = \dfrac{v_o}{v_n}$.

Common mode gain normally has a very low value, the lower - the better.

5.6 Common mode rejection ratio CMRR

This is a measure of an op-amp's ability to reject common mode signals and is normally quoted in dBs.

$$CMRR = 20 \log_{10} \frac{A_{DM}}{A_{CM}} \text{ dB}$$

Note: For a 741 op-amp the CMRR is 90 dB.

Example 5.3

In a differential amplifier circuit R_f = 10 kΩ and R_{in} = 1 kΩ. If the op-amp used is a 741, (a) find the common mode gain of the circuit and (b) if the common mode noise input is 10 volts, find the common mode noise output.

(a)

$$A_{DM} = -\frac{R_f}{R_{in}} = \mathbf{-10}$$

$$CMRR = 20 \, log_{10} \left(-\frac{10}{A_{CM}} \right)$$

$$90 = 20 \, log_{10} \left(-\frac{10}{A_{CM}} \right)$$

$$\frac{90}{20} = log_{10} \left(-\frac{10}{A_{CM}} \right)$$

$$4.5 = log_{10} \left(-\frac{10}{A_{CM}} \right)$$

antilog each side

$$10^{4.5} = -\frac{10}{A_{CM}}$$

$$31623 = -\frac{10}{A_{CM}}$$

$$A_{CM} = -\frac{10}{31623}$$

$$\underline{A_{CM} = -316 \times 10^{-6}}$$

(b)

$$\underline{\mathbf{\mathit{V_{\alpha(n)} = 3.16 \, mV}}}$$

Example 5.4

$R_f = 100\ k\Omega$, $R_i = 2\ k\Omega$, v_{AB} *(signal)* $= 5\ mV$, $v_n = 20\ mV$, *op-amp* $=$ *741. Calculate (a)* v_o *(signal)　(b)* v_o *(noise)*

$$A_{DM} = -\frac{100 \times 10^3}{2 \times 10^3} = -50$$

(a)

$$v_o\,(signal\,) = 50 \times 5 \times 10^{-3} = \underline{\textbf{250 mV}}$$

(b)

$$CMRR = 20\ log_{10}\left(\frac{-50}{A_{CM}}\right)$$

$$\frac{90}{20} = log_{10}\left(\frac{-50}{A_{CM}}\right)$$

$$4.5 = log_{10}\left(\frac{-50}{A_{CM}}\right)$$

$$10^{4.5} = \frac{-50}{A_{CM}}$$

$$31623 = \frac{-50}{A_{CM}}$$

$$A_{CM} = \frac{-50}{31623}$$

$$\underline{\textbf{A}_{CM} = \textbf{1.58} \times \textbf{10}^{-3}}$$

for v_{in} *(noise)* $= 20\ mV$,

$$v_{o\,(noise)} = 20 \times 10^{-3} \times 1.58 \times 10^{-3}$$

$$\underline{\textbf{v}_{o\,(noise)} = \textbf{31.6}\,\mu\textbf{V}}$$

6 Applications of Op-amps

In addition to the inverting and non-inverting amplifiers described in the previous chapter there are a number of applications of operational amplifiers that require special circuit configurations. These include:

- □ summing amplifier
- □ difference amplifier
- □ differentiator
- □ integrator
- □ voltage comparator

Of these, the summing amplifier, the difference (or differential) amplifier, the voltage comparator and the integrator will be examined in this chapter; the differentiator is considered not especially relevant to higher level courses. The summing amplifier and the difference amplifier (or subtractor) work on the principles outlined for inverting and non-inverting amplifiers in earlier work.

6.1 The summing amplifier

This commonly-used circuit, often referred to as a voltage or current adder, employs an op-amp-based inverting amplifier, illustrated in figure 6.1. The operation of the circuit relies upon the assumption that the ideal op-amp will have no current flowing in its input terminals (point 'x' is often referred to as the 'summing junction'). The **sum** of the currents flowing in the input resistors must flow in R_f, therefore

$$i_f = i_1 + i_2 + i_3$$

The inclusion of series resistors in the circuit means that voltages may be added, so

$$\frac{V_1}{R_1} + \frac{V_2}{R_2} + \frac{V_3}{R_3} = -\frac{V_0}{R_f}$$

and

$$V_0 = -R_f \left(\frac{V_1}{R_1} + \frac{V_2}{R_2} + \frac{V_3}{R_3} \right)$$

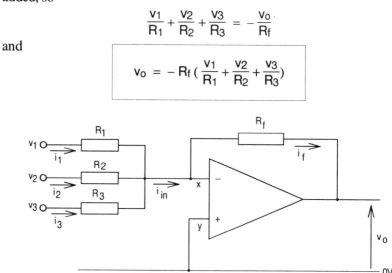

Figure 6.1 *The summing amplifier*

The summing amplifier can be used in any circuit where analogue voltages or currents have to be added. One specific use for the circuit is in a simple, but not commercially popular, digital to analogue converter (DAC).

6.1.1 Digital to analogue converter

Consider a 4-input summing amplifier to which 4 digital signals with an 8-4-2-1 weighting are applied. The values of the 4 input resistors must reflect the weighting of the digital signals, hence the Most Significant Bit (MSB) must be amplified 8 times that of the Least Significant Bit (LSB). The circuit illustrated in figure 6.2 employs input resistors with values of 8 kΩ, 4 kΩ, 2 kΩ and 1 kΩ. The value of the feedback resistor is dependent upon the need for gain (or attenuation) from the converter.

Note that the MSB is applied to the 1 kΩ resistor and the LSB to the 8 kΩ resistor, providing the necessary gain weighting for the converter. Note

also that the circuit is not commercially popular because the values of resistance required are not preferred. Moreover, if, for example, 16 binary digits were being used, the range of input resistance would be extremely large, leading to considerable errors in the resulting analogue output voltage. The inversion produced by the summing amplifier can, of course, be removed by the use of a further stage of amplification or buffering (it is not possible to use a non-inverting amplifier in the summing circuit).

Example 6.1

A digital to analogue converter employs a summing amplifier with the following component values, Rf = 1.6 kΩ, R1 (LSB) = 8.0 kΩ, R2 = 4.0 kΩ, R3 = 2.0 kΩ and R4 (MSB) = 1 kΩ. If the applied digital signals have a value of 0 V for a logic 0 and +5 V for a logic 1, calculate the analogue output voltage if binary 1001 (decimal 9) is applied to the inputs.

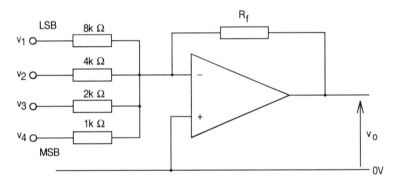

Figure 6.2 4-bit DAC using summing amplifier

$$V_o = -R_f \left(\frac{V_1}{R_1} + \frac{V_2}{R_2} + \frac{V_3}{R_3} + \frac{V_4}{R_4} \right)$$

$$V_o = -1.6 \times 10^3 \left(\frac{5}{8 \times 10^3} + \frac{0}{4 \times 10^3} + \frac{0}{2 \times 10^3} + \frac{5}{1 \times 10^3} \right)$$

$$V_o = -1.6 \left(\frac{5}{8} + 0 + 0 + \frac{5}{1} \right)$$

$$\underline{V_o = -9\ V}$$

6.2 The subtracting amplifier

In chapter 5 the differential or difference amplifier was introduced and analysed. The production of the difference between two signals is, of course, the process of subtraction and the differential amplifier is used for that purpose. Figure 6.3 shows such a circuit in which a single voltage is subtracted from another single voltage.

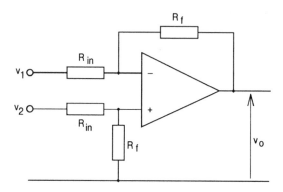

Figure 6.3 *A simple subtractor circuit*

The output voltage, v_o, is a function of the applied input signals and input resistors such that

$$v_o = \frac{R_f}{R_{in}} (v_2 - v_1)$$

where both input resistors and both feedback resistors are equal in value.

In practical situations it is likely that several signals would be applied to each of the inputs, with different weightings of input resistor, solving a much more complex arithmetic problem.

6.3 The voltage comparator

One of the most popular uses of an operational amplifier is as an analogue voltage comparator. The comparator employs the very high open-loop gain of the op-amp to produce a saturated output, positive or negative-going. For an alternating input signal this would produce a square wave output, or, for a slowly rising or falling input voltage, a rapidly switching output.

The many uses of a voltage comparator include:

- □   reconstituting degraded pulses
- □   sensing a specific voltage level
- □   squaring a sine or triangular waveform
- □   driving switching circuits
- □   interfacing to digital circuits

In order to achieve maximum efficiency, a comparator must use an op-amp that is designed to operate best in open-loop mode (most op-amps for linear applications are designed to work best under closed-loop conditions, i.e. with frequency/phase compensation).

Note: Although any op-amp can be configured as a comparator, any with internal frequency compensation will have a slower response time and may not perform adequately under certain conditions.

A voltage comparator is most efficient if the parameters of the operational amplifier employed in the circuit are as close to an ideal op-amp as possible.

To operate as a voltage comparator, one input of the op-amp must be connected to a fixed 'reference' source. The other terminal is supplied with the signal that is to be processed. In many circuits the reference point is at ground potential (0 V). One name given to this circuit is the 'zero-crossing detector', as it detects the point at which the applied signal rises above, or falls below, zero volts.

It should be noted that, as with linear amplifiers, comparators may be inverting or non-inverting types.

Consider figure 6.4.

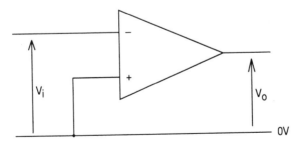

Figure 6.4 *Inverting zero-crossing detector*

The non-inverting terminal of the comparator is connected to 0 V. A signal is applied to the inverting terminal. There is no feedback of any description connected to the comparator and, therefore, it is operating under open-loop conditions. If, for example, the comparator was constructed using a 741 op-amp, its open-loop voltage gain would be 106 dB (approximately 200,000). If it was connected to supply rails of +15 V and −15 V, its output would swing between approximately +14.5 V and −14.5 V, a total swing of around 29 volts. With a gain of 200,000 an input swing of approximately 145 μV is all that would be needed to make the output saturate. As the input signal is connected to the inverting terminal of the comparator, a negative input voltage will cause the output to be positive. If that input is lower than −72.5 μV, the output will be saturated in a positive manner.

A transfer characteristic is employed to illustrate the relationship between input and output signals. Figure 6.5 shows the characteristic for the circuit in figure 6.4. The 145 μV 'window' is not shown on this diagram as it is extremely small in comparison with other circuit voltages.

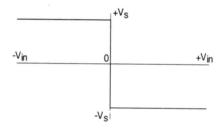

Figure 6.5 *Transfer characteristic*

The circuit arrangement and transfer characteristic for a non-inverting zero-crossing detector are shown in figures 6.6 and 6.7 respectively.

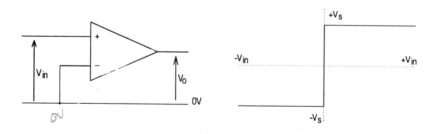

Figure 6.6 *Non-inverting detector*   **Figure 6.7 *Transfer characteristic***

Of course, it is possible to use a reference voltage that is not at zero volts. The reference point can be either positive or negative with respect to ground. A popular name for this type of circuit is a 'threshold detector'.

The next pair of figures, 6.8 and 6.9, show the circuit and transfer characteristic for a non-inverting threshold detector with negative V_{ref}, .

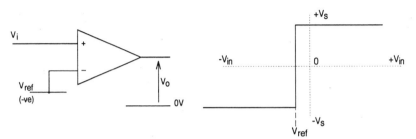

Figure 6.8 *Non-inverting, -ve Vref*   **Figure 6.9 *Transfer characteristic***

Figures 6.10 and 6.11 illustrate the circuit arrangement and transfer characteristic for an inverting comparator with a positive reference voltage.

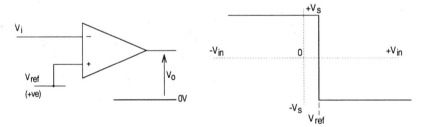

Figure 6.10 *Inverting, +ve Vref*   **Figure 6.11 *Transfer characteristic***

There are, of course, transfer characteristics for positive reference voltage with non-inverting action and negative reference with inverting action, but these are not shown.

Note that the characteristics do not show a time-related change from one saturated state to the other. The time taken for the output to change state produces a non-vertical edge to the output switching waveform, the 'slope' of which is dependent upon the slew rate of the operational amplifier/comparator in use.

For example, the slew rate for a 741 op-amp is 500,000 volts per second. A change in output voltage from +10 V to −10 V would take

$$\frac{20 \times 10^6}{5 \times 10^5} \, \mu s \;=\; \frac{20}{0.5} \;=\; \underline{\mathbf{40 \; \mu s}}$$

There are two significant limitations to the successful operation of a voltage comparator. If the input voltage changes very slowly the rate of change of the output will also be very slow. The op-amp will be operating as a linear amplifier, an effect that is undesirable.

A second limitation on the use of the simple circuits so far discussed is the effect that noise (or hum) on the input signal produces. Consider a rising input voltage upon which a substantial 'hum' is superimposed.

False switching, 'chattering' or 'chopping' of the output is caused by the effective input voltage (signal + noise) repeatedly crossing the reference point, as illustrated in figure 6.12.

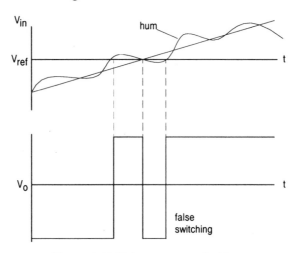

Figure 6.12 *False output switching*

In addition to the problem of hum, other transient or interference signals can cause similar problems. In the case of a very slowly-changing input signal, it is possible to increase the speed of output switching.

The solution to both of these 'problems' is to introduce some positive feedback into the circuit, thus forming a regenerative voltage comparator having 'hysteresis'. In addition to speeding up the switching action, positive feedback produces different reference levels for positive-going and negative-going transitions, resulting in separate upper and lower threshold levels. The difference between the two threshold levels is the hysteresis voltage or 'window'.

In most practical applications a compromise must be found between a large hysteresis 'window' to reject any noise present and a small window to make the switching circuit sensitive enough for accurate level detection.

6.3.1 Comparators with hysteresis

Consider a non-inverting comparator having a reference voltage of zero volts, the circuit of which is shown in figure 6.13.

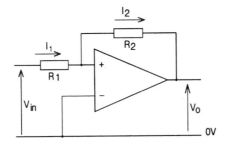

Figure 6.13 *Comparator with hysteresis*

A feedback voltage is derived from the output and applied, via a resistor (R_2), to the non-inverting input terminal (i.e. positive feedback). In order to prevent this feedback affecting the original input signal, a series resistor (R_1) is inserted in the signal path.

Suppose that V_{in} is a slowly-rising voltage. The voltage on the non-inverting terminal also increases slowly, producing a corresponding, but much larger, increase in V_o. A fraction of V_o is fed back to the non-inverting input, causing a further increase in the signal amplitude at that point. In this way, the slowly-rising input is changed into a much faster-rising signal. Figure 6.14 shows the transfer characteristic for a non-inverting comparator with hysteresis and a reference voltage of zero volts.

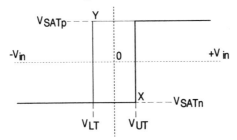

Figure 6.14 *Hysteresis characteristic*

V_{LT}:   **Lower threshold voltage (input).**

V_{UT}:   **Upper threshold voltage (input).**

V_{SATp}: **Positive saturation voltage (output).**

V_{SATn}: **Negative saturation voltage (output).**

In order to analyse the circuit in figure 6.13, it is necessary to consider an ideal operational amplifier, as described earlier, and the passive components R_1 and R_2. Ideally, the current flowing in the op-amp terminals will be zero. Therefore any current flowing in R_1 (I_1) will also flow in R_2 (I_2), i.e. $I_1 = I_2$.

Consider point X (Figure 6.14).

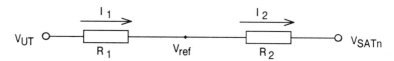

Figure 6.15 *Circuit voltages (point X)*

As V_{UT} will be more positive than V_{SATn}, conventional current flow will be as indicated in figure 6.15. The junction of R_1 and R_2 will effectively be at the same potential as the inverting input, i.e. V_{ref}.

$$I_1 = \frac{(V_{UT} - V_{ref})}{R_1} \quad \text{and} \quad I_2 = \frac{(V_{ref} - V_{SATn})}{R_2}$$

as $I_1 = I_2$ then

$$\frac{(V_{UT} - V_{ref})}{R_1} = \frac{(V_{ref} - V_{SATn})}{R_2}$$

$$V_{UT} - V_{ref} = \frac{R_1 V_{ref}}{R_2} - \frac{V_{SATn} R_1}{R_2}$$

$$V_{UT} = V_{ref} + V_{ref}\frac{R_1}{R_2} - \frac{V_{SATn} R_1}{R_2}$$

$$V_{UT} = V_{ref}\left(1 + \frac{R_1}{R_2}\right) - \frac{V_{SATn} R_1}{R_2}$$

However, if $V_{ref} = 0$ V, the term containing V_{ref} disappears and

$$V_{UT} = -V_{SATn} \frac{R_1}{R_2}$$

Consider Point Y (Figure 6.14).

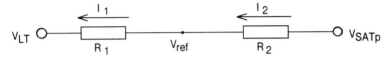

Figure 6.16 *Circuit voltages (point Y)*

$$\frac{V_{SATp} - V_{ref}}{R_2} = \frac{V_{ref} - V_{LT}}{R_1}$$

$$\frac{V_{SATp} R_1}{R_2} - \frac{V_{ref} R_1}{R_2} = V_{ref} - V_{LT}$$

$$V_{LT} = V_{ref} - \frac{V_{SATp} R_1}{R_2} + \frac{V_{ref} R_1}{R_2}$$

$$V_{LT} = V_{ref} + \frac{V_{ref} R_1}{R_2} - \frac{V_{SATp} R_1}{R_2}$$

$$V_{LT} = V_{ref} \left(1 + \frac{R_1}{R_2} \right) - \frac{V_{SATp} R_1}{R_2}$$

However, if $V_{ref} = 0$ V,

$$V_{LT} = -V_{SATp} \frac{R_1}{R_2}$$

The hysteresis voltage, V_{HYS}, is the difference between V_{UT} and V_{LT}.

$$V_{HYS} = V_{UT} - V_{LT}$$

Example 6.2

If $V_{SATp} = +12\ V$, $V_{SATn} = -12\ V$, $R_1 = 1\ k\Omega$ and $R_2 = 10\ k\Omega$, calculate V_{UT} and V_{LT}.

$$V_{UT} = -\frac{-12\ x\ 1}{10} = --1.2 \qquad \underline{= +\textbf{ 1.2 volts}}$$

$$V_{LT} = -\frac{+12\ x\ 1}{10} = -1.2 \qquad \underline{= -\textbf{ 1.2 volts}}$$

Example 6.3

If V_{SATp} and $V_{SATn} = \pm 10\ V$, $V_{ref} = +2\ V$, $R_1 = 1\ k\Omega$ and $R_2 = 10\ k\Omega$, calculate V_{UT} and V_{LT}.

$$V_{UT} = 2\,(\,1 + 0.1\,) - \frac{-10}{10}$$

$$\underline{V_{UT} = +\textbf{ 3.2 volts}}$$

$$V_{LT} = 2\,(\,1 + 0.1\,) - \frac{10}{10}$$

$$\underline{V_{LT} = +\textbf{ 1.2 volts}}$$

Example 6.4

If a hysteresis window of 8.46 V is required centred about 0 V, design a suitable comparator, assuming that $V_{SATp} = +18\ V$, $V_{SATn} = -18\ V$ and $R_2 = 20\ k\Omega$.

$$\frac{V_{UT}}{R_1} = -\frac{V_{SATn}}{R_2}$$

$$R_1 = -\frac{V_{UT}\ R_2}{V_{SATn}} = \frac{-4.23\ x\ 20\ x\ 10^3}{-18}$$

$$\underline{R_1 = \textbf{ 4.7 k}\Omega}$$

6.3.2 The inverting comparator

So far all of the voltage comparators with hysteresis have had a non-inverting action. The inverting comparator with hysteresis will now be considered. The diagram in figure 6.17 illustrates the circuit arrangement.

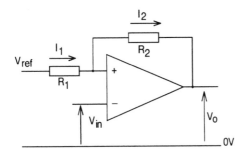

Figure 6.17 *Inverting comparator with hysteresis*

The transfer characteristic is as shown in figure 6.18.

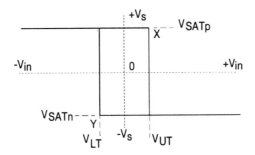

Figure 6.18 *Transfer characteristic*

As with the non-inverting comparator, analysis at this level assumes an ideal op-amp.

Consider point X (Figure 6.18)

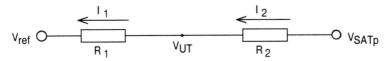

Figure 6.19 *Circuit conditions at point X*

For an ideal op-amp, $I_1 = I_2$, therefore

$$\frac{V_{SATp} - V_{UT}}{R_2} = \frac{V_{UT} - V_{ref}}{R_1}$$

$$\frac{V_{SATp}}{R_2} - \frac{V_{UT}}{R_2} = \frac{V_{UT}}{R_1} - \frac{V_{ref}}{R_1}$$

$$\frac{V_{UT}}{R_1} + \frac{V_{UT}}{R_2} = \frac{V_{SATp}}{R_2} + \frac{V_{ref}}{R_1}$$

multiply each term by $R_1 R_2$

$$\frac{V_{UT} R_1 R_2}{R_1} + \frac{V_{UT} R_1 R_2}{R_2} = \frac{V_{SATp} R_1 R_2}{R_2} + \frac{V_{ref} R_1 R_2}{R_1}$$

$$V_{UT} R_2 + V_{UT} R_1 = V_{SATp} R_1 + V_{ref} R_2$$

$$V_{UT} (R_1 + R_2) = V_{SATp} R_1 + V_{ref} R_2$$

$$\boxed{V_{UT} = \frac{V_{SATp} R_1 + V_{ref} R_2}{(R_1 + R_2)}}$$

But, if $V_{ref} = 0$ V, then

$$\boxed{V_{UT} = \frac{V_{SATp} R_1}{(R_1 + R_2)}}$$

Analysis of the circuit conditions at point Y on figure 6.18 will follow those for point X except that V_{SATn} will replace V_{SATp} and V_{LT} will be found instead of V_{UT}. The final expression for V_{LT} is

$$\boxed{V_{LT} = \frac{V_{SATn} R_1 + V_{ref} R_2}{(R_1 + R_2)}}$$

or, if $V_{ref} = 0$ V

$$\boxed{V_{LT} = \frac{V_{SATn} R_1}{(R_1 + R_2)}}$$

6.4 The integrator

Consider the circuit shown in figure 6.20.

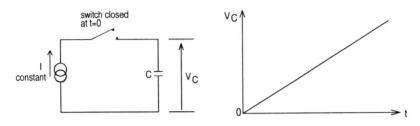

Figure 6.20 *Capacitor charging circuit*   **Figure 6.21** V_c *against time*

With a **constant current supply**, the charge (Q) on the capacitor (C) is a linear function of the current (I) and the elapsed time (t).

$$Q = I\ t$$

$$\text{and}\ \ Q = C\ V_C$$

therefore,

$$C\ V_C = I\ t$$

and

$$V_C = \frac{I\ t}{C}$$

Note that the graph of V_C against time is not exponential as with a capacitor charging through a resistor. In the R-C charging circuit the current supplying the capacitor would be falling exponentially.

Example 6.5

If $I = 1$ μA, $C = 1$ μF and $t = 5$ s, calculate V_C.

$$V_C = \frac{1 \times 10^{-6} \times 5}{1 \times 10^{-6}} = \underline{\mathbf{5\ volts}}$$

As the rate of rise in current is linear, a change of 5 V over 5 seconds equals a rate of 1 V/s.

Consider an operational amplifier circuit as illustrated in figure 6.22.

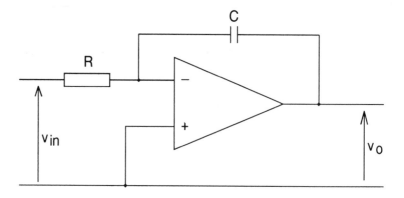

Figure 6.22 *Op-amp integrator circuit*

Any current flowing into C via R (due to a positive v_{in}), will make C charge in a positive manner. However, as the inverting terminal of the op-amp is a virtual earth, the 'output end' of the capacitor must go negative with respect to ground. Consequently a positive v_{in} results in a negative-going v_o. The rate at which the output goes negative is dependent upon the level of v_{in} (for given values of R and C), the higher the level - the greater the rate of change of v_o. When $v_{in} = 0$ V, v_o remains steady at its present level. In order to calculate the rate of change of the output of the circuit in figure 6.22, it is necessary to combine the expression for V_C derived earlier and that for current in a resistive circuit.

From $V_C = \dfrac{I\,t}{C}$ and $I = \dfrac{V_{in}}{R}$

$$V_C = \frac{V_{in}\,t}{C\,R}$$

As v_o is the inverse of V_C

$$\boxed{v_o = -\frac{V_{in}\,t}{C\,R}}$$

The diagram in figure 6.23 illustrates the relationship between positive, zero and negative input voltages and the resulting output waveform.

Note that vo starts at an arbitrary level.

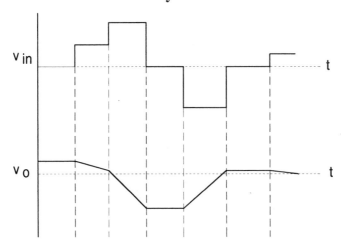

Figure 6.23 *Integrator waveforms*

Example 6.6

If $C = 1\ \mu F$ and $R = 10\ k\Omega$, sketch the time-related waveforms for v_{in} and v_o if v_{in} starts at 0 V and changes to +10 V (start v_o at 5 V).

$$v_o = -\frac{V_{in}\,t}{C\,R}$$

if t = 10 ms, then

$$V_O = \frac{10 \times 10 \times 10^{-3}}{1 \times 10^{-6} \times 10 \times 10^{3}}$$

equals a rate of 10 V over 10 ms, or 1 V/ms

If v_O starts at +5 V then after 10 ms it will have fallen to −5 V.

Example 6.7

For a square wave input of ±10 V and a periodic time of 20 ms, draw time-related waveforms of v_{in} and v_O for the integrator in example 6.6.

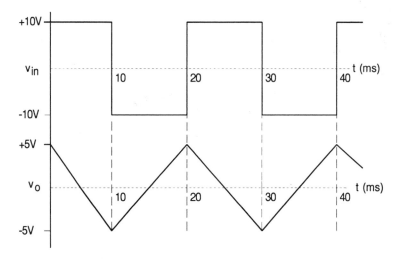

Figure 6.24 *Waveform for example 6.7*

Example 6.7 indicates a use for this type of circuit, that is, to produce triangular waves from square waves. A circuit that produces triangular and square waves could be used as a function generator. In practice, most such generators are also capable of producing a sine wave output, although this is rarely a pure sine wave. Instead, an approximation to a sine wave can be 'synthesised' from a triangular waveform. Such circuits will be illustrated and described in chapter 8 - Waveform Generators.

7 Feedback

The subject of feedback will have been encountered during lower level studies, as well as being mentioned, albeit very briefly, in chapter 6 (Applications of Op-amps). Feedback occurs, by design or otherwise, when a proportion of the output signal of a given circuit is applied to the input of the same circuit. The effect of the feedback upon the performance of the circuit, usually an amplifier, is determined by two factors; the magnitude of the feedback signal and its phase relative to the input signal.

In general, feedback is referred to as 'negative' or 'positive' with respect to the input. However, this description is too simplistic for higher level studies as it implies that the situation is clear-cut and unambiguous. For a single-stage amplifier it is relatively straightforward to determine the phase, and consequently the effect of, any feedback present. However, when multistage amplifiers are considered, some inverting and others non-inverting, the situation is anything but straightforward.

This chapter will start by reviewing some of the lower level work on negative feedback and progress to the analysis of amplifiers with feedback and examination of the Nyquist criterion (a means of determining the effect of feedback on a multi-stage amplifier). Our main area of interest is that of negative feedback, employed mainly to improve the performance of an amplifier. Positive feedback is generally used if a circuit is required to be unstable, for example to produce oscillations. The subject of positive feedback in general and oscillators in particular will be dealt with in chapter 8 of this book.

If a signal that opposes the input signal is applied to the input of an amplifier then the effective input signal amplitude will be reduced and, consequently, so will that of the output signal amplitude. Clearly, negative feedback causes an effective reduction in gain of an amplifier. However, there are many advantages to be gained from negative feedback, for example

- ❑ increased bandwidth
- ❑ increased gain stability
- ❑ reduced noise
- ❑ reduced amplitude/frequency distortion
- ❑ reduced distortion due to non-linearity of amplifier characteristics

The manner in which feedback is first derived from the output of a circuit and then applied to its input leads to further modification of the amplifier's performance.

7.1 Deriving an expression for gain with feedback

Figure 7.1 shows the general block diagram for an amplifier and feedback network. The open-loop gain of the amplifier is termed A_o.

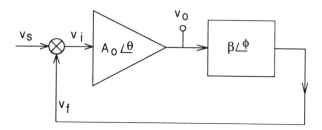

Figure 7.1 *Basic feedback arrangement*

The amplifier has a gain of $A_o \angle\theta$, such that

$$v_o = v_i A_o \angle\theta$$

and the feedback network has a value that is a fraction, $\beta \angle\phi$, of the output voltage, therefore

$$v_f = v_o \beta \angle\phi$$

$$\therefore v_f = v_i A_o \angle\theta \beta \angle\phi$$

For the purposes of study at this level and, therefore, this book, the feedback network may be considered to be resistive only, that is ϕ has an angle of $0°$.

The input voltage to the amplifier, v_i, is the sum of the two voltages applied to the summing junction, i.e.

$$v_i = v_s + v_f$$

$$\therefore v_s = v_i - v_f$$

But $v_i = \dfrac{v_o}{A_o \angle \theta}$ and $v_f = v_o \beta$, so

$$v_s = \frac{v_o}{A_o \angle \theta} - v_o \beta$$

Taking v_o out of each expression gives

$$v_s = v_o \left(\frac{1}{A_o \angle \theta} - \beta \right)$$

If both sides of the expression are multiplied by $A_o \angle \theta$, then

$$v_s A_o \angle \theta = v_o \left(\frac{A_o \angle \theta}{A_o \angle \theta} - A_o \beta \angle \theta \right)$$

$$v_s A_o \angle \theta = v_o (1 - A_o \beta \angle \theta)$$

$$\frac{v_s}{v_o} = \frac{(1 - A_o \beta \angle \theta)}{A_o \angle \theta}$$

but A_f, gain with feedback, $= \dfrac{v_o}{v_s}$, therefore

$$A_f = \frac{v_o}{v_s} = \frac{A_o \angle \theta}{(1 - A_o \beta \angle \theta)}$$

Note that the expression $1 - A_o \beta \angle \theta$ is often termed the 'return difference' and appears in all expressions relating to gain and input and output impedances of an amplifier with negative feedback applied.

Example 7.1

Figure 7.2 illustrates a typical amplifier and feedback network combination. Calculate the voltage gain with negative feedback applied.

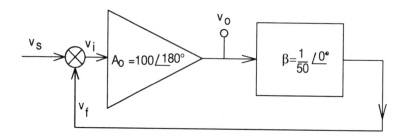

Figure 7.2 *Diagram for example 7.1*

In this arrangement the feedback is negative with respect to the input signal. The angle of the fed back signal is 180° and may be shown with a minus sign and no angle

$$A_f = \frac{A_o \angle \theta}{1 - - A_o \beta}$$

$$A_f = \frac{100 \angle 180°}{1 + (100 \times \frac{1}{50})}$$

$$A_f = \frac{100 \angle 180°}{3}$$

$$\underline{A_f = 33.3 \angle 180°}$$

7.2 Derivation and application of feedback

There are two basic means of derivation and two basic means of application, giving four possible feedback derivation/application combinations.

The required feedback signal may be derived by connecting a sampling circuit in parallel (or shunt) with the load, known as shunt or voltage derived feedback, or by inserting the sampling circuit in series with the load, known as series or current derived feedback.

Similarly, the feedback signal may be applied in shunt or in series with the input signal. Figures 7.3, 7.4, 7.5 and 7.6 illustrate, in simple block diagram form, the four combinations.

Note that, in this text, the form of derivation is placed first, followed by the means of application.

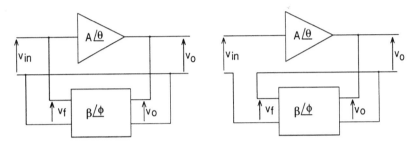

       Figure 7.3 *Shunt-shunt*   **Figure 7.4** *Shunt-series*

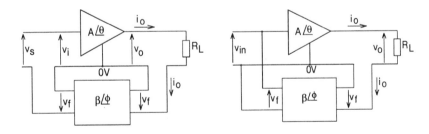

      Figure 7.5 *Series-series*   **Figure 7.6** *Series-shunt*

7.2.1 Shunt derivation

In this means of feedback derivation a voltage is obtained by connecting the feedback sampling circuit in shunt with the output voltage. The effect of this connection is to decrease the output impedance of the circuit.

It can be proved that the output impedance of an amplifier with negative feedback is a function of the open-loop impedance and the 'return difference', $1 - A_o \beta$.

$$Z_{o(f)} = \frac{Z_o}{1 - A_o \beta}$$

In practice, the feedback network has very little effect on the output of the circuit owing to its impedance being much higher than that of the load.

7.2.2 Series derivation

When the feedback sensing circuit is placed in series with the load it is the level of output current that determines the amount of feedback that is derived. The effect of series, or current, derivation is to increase the output impedance of the circuit as the resistance of the feedback sensing circuit is in series with the load. Note the presence of the return difference.

$$Z_{o(f)} = Z_o (1 - A_o \beta)$$

7.2.3 Shunt application

The application of negative feedback in shunt with the input signal has the effect of reducing both the signal to the amplifier and the input impedance of the amplifier. Again, the 'return difference' is used in the expression.

$$Z_{in(f)} = \frac{Z_{in}}{(1 - A_o \beta)}$$

7.2.4 Series application

Series application increases the input impedance of the amplifier

$$Z_{in(f)} = Z_{in} (1 - A_o \beta)$$

Remember that the 'return difference' has a value greater than 1 as the applied feedback is *negative.*

7.3 Practical feedback circuits

7.3.1 Shunt-derived series-applied

Consider the amplifier in figure 7.7. The feedback voltage is developed across a potential divider circuit connected across the load, R_L. A fraction of the output voltage will appear across R_B, that fraction being determined by the ratio $\dfrac{R_B}{R_A + R_B}$. The feedback voltage, v_f, will be that fraction of v_o.

$$v_f = v_o \left(\frac{R_B}{R_A + R_B}\right)$$

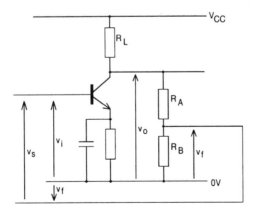

Figure 7.7 *Shunt-derived series-applied*

The inclusion of $R_A + R_B$ in parallel with R_L has the effect of lowering the output impedance of the amplifier. However, in practice, the effective resistance $R_A + R_B$ is generally much higher than R_L, making their impact minimal. Application of feedback is in series with the input signal, increasing the effective input impedance. Analysis of this circuit can be performed with the aid of an h-parameter equivalent circuit, see figure 7.8.

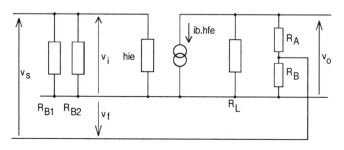

Figure 7.8 *h-parameter equivalent circuit*

Although a slight error is introduced, it is beneficial to circuit analysis if the combined resistance $R_A + R_B$ is considered to be very much greater than R_L. It can then be assumed that all of the current $i_b\, h_{fe}$ will flow in R_L. So

$$\text{Gain with feedback } (A_f) = \frac{v_o}{v_s}$$

$$v_o = -h_{fe}\, i_b\, R_L$$

$$v_s = v_i - v_f$$

$$v_i = i_b\, h_{ie}$$

$$v_f = \beta\, v_o \text{ where } \beta = \frac{R_B}{R_A + R_B}$$

$$v_f = -h_{fe}\, i_b\, R_L\, \beta$$

$$\text{so } \frac{v_o}{v_s} = \frac{-h_{fe}\, i_b\, R_L}{i_b\, h_{ie} -- i_b\, h_{fe}\, R_L\, \beta}$$

i_bs cancel, so $\boxed{A_f = \dfrac{v_o}{v_s} = \dfrac{-h_{fe}\, R_L}{h_{ie} + h_{fe}\, R_L\, \beta}}$

This expression for gain with feedback may be stated in the standard form if each term is divided by h_{ie}

$$A_f = \frac{\dfrac{-h_{fe} R_L}{h_{ie}}}{\dfrac{h_{ie}}{h_{ie}} + \dfrac{h_{fe} R_L \beta}{h_{ie}}}$$

$$\text{now} \quad \frac{-h_{fe} R_L}{h_{ie}} = A_o$$

$$\text{and} \quad \frac{h_{ie}}{h_{ie}} = 1$$

$$\boxed{A_f = \frac{A_o}{1 - A_o \beta}}$$

The input impedance can be determined by reverting to Ohm's Law

$$Z_{in} = \frac{v_i}{i_b}$$

$$Z_{in} = \frac{i_b h_{ie} + h_{fe} i_b R_L \beta}{i_b}$$

again, i_bs cancel, so

$$\boxed{Z_{in} = h_{ie} + h_{fe} R_L \beta}$$

To express Z_{in} in the general terms indicated earlier, both sides of the expression are divided by h_{ie}.

$$\frac{Z_{in}}{h_{ie}} = \frac{h_{ie}}{h_{ie}} + \frac{h_{fe} R_L \beta}{h_{ie}}$$

$$\frac{Z_{in}}{h_{ie}} = 1 - A_o \beta$$

$$\boxed{Z_{in} = h_{ie} (1 - A_o \beta)}$$

The output impedance of the circuit is measured with the input terminals short-circuited. A voltage is applied across the output terminals and the current flowing in the output is measured and recorded. The impedance is then found from

$$Z_o = \frac{v_o}{i_o}$$

An h-parameter equivalent circuit, as shown in figure 7.9, may be used in order to derive the expression for Z_o.

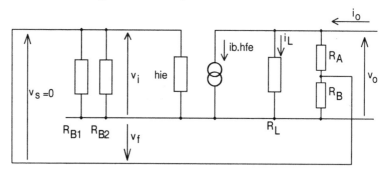

Figure 7.9 *Arrangement for deriving Z_o*

In order to derive the expression for Z_o, it may be assumed, as in the earlier derivation of amplifier gain, that the current in $R_A + R_B$ is negligible. The current driven into the output terminals, i_o, will divide between that flowing in R_L and $h_{fe} i_b$.

If the current flowing in R_L is termed i_L, then

$$i_L = \frac{v_o}{R_L}$$

$$i_o = i_L + h_{fe} i_b$$

$$i_o = \frac{v_o}{R_L} + h_{fe} i_b \quad \ldots \ldots (1)$$

The feedback voltage, v_f, is a fraction of v_o, i.e.

$$v_f = \beta v_o$$

As $v_i - v_f = 0$, $v_i = v_f$, therefore

$$v_i = \beta v_o$$

substituting $v_i = \beta v_o$ into $i_b = \dfrac{v_i}{h_{ie}}$ gives

$$i_b = \frac{\beta v_o}{h_{ie}} \quad \dots\dots (2)$$

Substituting (2) into (1) gives

$$i_o = \frac{v_o}{R_L} + \frac{h_{fe}\,\beta\,v_o}{h_{ie}}$$

$$i_o = v_o \left(\frac{1}{R_L} + \frac{h_{fe}\,\beta}{h_{ie}} \right)$$

$$\frac{i_o}{v_o} = \frac{1}{R_L} + \frac{h_{fe}\,\beta}{h_{ie}}$$

But $Z_o = \dfrac{v_o}{i_o}$, therefore

$$Z_o = \frac{1}{\dfrac{1}{R_L} + \dfrac{h_{fe}\,\beta}{h_{ie}}}$$

To express in general terms, multiply top and bottom by R_L

$$Z_o = \frac{R_L}{\dfrac{R_L}{R_L} + \dfrac{h_{fe}\,R_L\,\beta}{h_{ie}}}$$

But $\dfrac{h_{fe}\,R_L}{h_{ie}} = -A_o$, so

$$Z_o = \frac{R_L}{1 - A_o\,\beta}$$

7.3.2 Series-derived series-applied

The standard arrangement for a common-emitter amplifier is to have an emitter resistor to prevent thermal runaway, with a parallel capacitor to bypass the resistor and prevent negative feedback. If the capacitor is omitted from the circuit then negative feedback is derived from the current flowing in the emitter circuit, i.e. the feedback is series-derived. The emitter resistor is effectively in series with the input resistance of the transistor so the feedback voltage developed across R_E will be in series with the applied input signal. Figure 7.10 illustrates the circuit and the relevant signals.

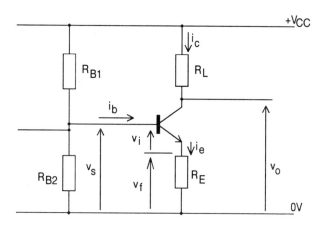

Figure 7.10 *Series-derived series-applied*

The voltage gain of this circuit can be derived from the h-parameter equivalent circuit illustrated in figure 7.11.

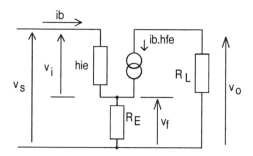

Figure 7.11 *Un-bypassed emitter*

From the equivalent circuit it can be seen that

$$v_s = i_b h_{ie} + i_b R_E + h_{fe} i_b R_E$$

as $h_{fe} i_b$ is $>> i_b$, the term $i_b R_E$ can be neglected, leaving

$$v_s = i_b h_{ie} + h_{fe} i_b R_E$$

Voltage gain, $A_v = \dfrac{v_o}{v_s}$

$$\frac{v_o}{v_s} = \frac{- R_L h_{fe} i_b}{i_b h_{ie} + h_{fe} i_b R_E}$$

i_bs cancel, leaving

$$\boxed{A_v = \frac{v_o}{v_s} = \frac{- R_L h_{fe}}{h_{ie} + R_E h_{fe}}}$$

Dividing top and bottom by h_{ie} gives

$$A_v = \frac{\dfrac{- R_L h_{fe}}{h_{ie}}}{\dfrac{h_{ie}}{h_{ie}} + \dfrac{R_E h_{fe}}{h_{ie}}}$$

As $\dfrac{- h_{fe} R_L}{h_{ie}} = A_o$

$$\boxed{A_v = \frac{A_o}{1 - \dfrac{A_o R_E}{R_L}}}$$

As the standard expression for gain with feedback, A_f, is $\dfrac{A_o}{1 - A_o \beta}$ it follows that, in this circuit, $\beta = \dfrac{R_E}{R_L}$

The feedback fraction, β, can be derived as follows

$$\beta = \frac{v_f}{v_o} = \frac{R_E \left(h_{fe} i_b + i_b \right)}{R_L h_{fe} i_b} \approx \frac{R_E}{R_L}$$

7.3.3 Shunt-derived shunt-applied

Consider the circuit diagram shown in figure 7.12. C_f has a fairly large value, in the order of μF and is required simply to block the d.c. potential on the collector from affecting the base biasing, whilst allowing the coupling of the a.c. feedback signal to R_f. A fraction of v_o is developed across R_f, i.e. shunt-derived, and applied to the base of the transistor in shunt with the input signal, i.e. shunt-applied.

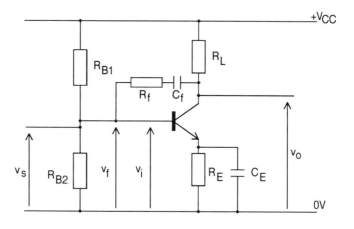

Figure 7.12 *Shunt-derived shunt-applied feedback*

7.3.4 Series-derived shunt-applied

This feedback arrangement, for transistor amplifiers anyway, is usually achieved with two stages of amplification. The feedback is derived in the same manner as that described for the series-derived series-applied arrangement, i.e. by the omission of the emitter decoupling capacitor, but from the second stage of amplification. The feedback voltage is then applied to the base of the first transistor.

Note that inversion of the signal occurs in T_1 only, the feedback signal being taken from the emitter of T_2. This ensures that feedback applied to T_1 base opposes the input signal (i.e. negative feedback).

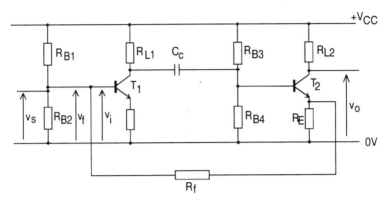

Figure 7.13 *Series-derived shunt-applied*

7.4 Feedback in multi-stage amplifiers

When feedback is used in multi-stage amplifiers, special attention has to be paid to the phase of the feedback signal relative to the input signal that it is applied to.

7.4.1 Two stages, one inverting - one non-inverting

Consider the amplifier arrangement shown in figure 7.14. The first stage of amplification inverts the signal but the second stage is non-inverting.

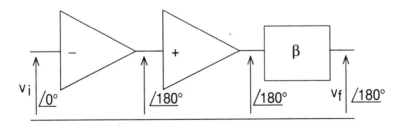

Figure 7.14 *2 stage amplifier phase relationship*

In this amplifier arrangement the feedback voltage, v_f, can never be equal to v_i. As a result this amplifier will be stable for all types of feedback at any frequency of operation. In order to make calculations easier, v_i is often termed the reference or critical point and given the value of $1\angle 0°$.

A Nyquist plot of A_f for the amplifier reveals that the locus does NOT enclose the reference point $1\angle 0°$ and it will be shown that it is this 'test' that determines whether a given amplifier arrangement will be stable or unstable. This test is called the 'Nyquist Criterion'.

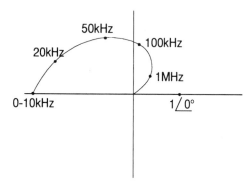

Figure 7.15 *Locus of A*f

7.4.2 Two-stage d.c. amplifier, both stages inverting

The block diagram for this circuit arrangement is shown in figure 7.16.

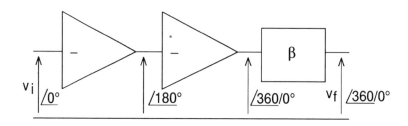

Figure 7.16 *2 stages, both inverting*

The feedback voltage will be in phase with the input signal and, as illustrated in figure 7.17, the locus of v_f will be greater in magnitude, and equal in phase to v_i. For that range of frequencies, i.e. 0 Hz to 10 kHz, the amplifier will be unstable, causing parasitic oscillation to occur.

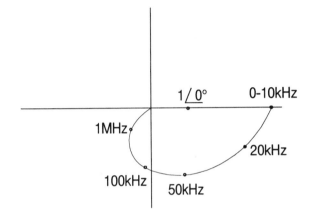

Figure 7.17 *Locus of v_f equals v_i*

7.4.3 Three stages - all inverting

If an amplifier employs three stages of inverting amplification the following Nyquist plot is obtained for v_f. In this example the locus of v_f encloses the reference point, again indicating that the amplifier is unstable at some frequency (about 1.2 MHz).

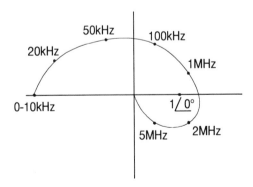

Figure 7.18 *Locus of v_f encloses v_i*

It can be seen that this circuit will become unstable and oscillate at a frequency around 1.2 MHz. However, if the amount of feedback applied were to be reduced, the locus would become smaller and could be arranged so as to **not** enclose the reference point.

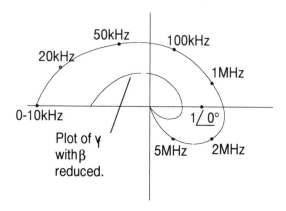

Figure 7.19 *Reduced feedback gives stability*

The last two examples form the basis of the Nyquist criterion which states that if the reference or critical point is equalled or enclosed by the locus of v_f then instability will be present at some frequency of operation.

Of course, in one field of electronics it is essential that the circuit is unstable - that of waveform generation. Chapter 8 discusses various circuits for the production of rectangular, triangular and sinusoidal waveforms.

8 Waveform Generators

In this chapter the subject of waveform generation will be considered, with circuits that generate sine, rectangular and triangular waveforms being analysed. In addition, a circuit that will synthesise a sine wave from a triangular waveform will be examined.

As seen in chapter 7, an amplifier that has feedback applied will become unstable if the locus of v_f equals or encloses the reference or critical point. This condition may also be described in terms of the loop gain of the circuit thus: if the loop gain of an amplifier is unity at an angle of 0°/360° then instability will arise, and oscillation will occur at some frequency.

Of course, in many applications, this is an undesirable situation which must be designed out of the circuit. However, if this condition can be arranged to occur then an oscillator (waveform generator) can be produced.

Of the three waveform shapes mentioned, only the sine wave is pure in as much as it comprises a single frequency only, with no harmonics present. The other wave shapes consist of combinations of harmonics, for example the square wave is formed from the 'odd' harmonics, i.e. 3rd, 5th, 7th, etc.

8.1 Sine wave oscillators

A pure sine wave can only be produced by 'ringing' a tuned circuit, R-C at low frequencies, L-C at high frequencies.

Many oscillator circuits are in use and this book will categorise them by frequency of operation.

An amplifier with feedback that is unstable because the loop gain $A_o \beta =$ +1 will oscillate at a single frequency, and will, therefore, produce a sine wave.

8.1.1 R-C oscillators

There is a requirement for a source of pure sine waves for test purposes. At high frequencies these signals are generated by L-C oscillators. However, at audio frequencies the inductor required becomes large and heavy, making R-C oscillators more acceptable.

Two common circuits will be considered, the phase shift oscillator and the Wien network oscillator. When designing an oscillator the engineer has to produce a circuit that has a gain of unity and feedback with a phase angle of 0° or 360°. This can be achieved in many ways but two basic arrangements are employed in most circuits. In one arrangement 180° phase shift is derived from an inverting amplifier (transistor or operational amplifier), with the remaining 180° coming from the tuned circuit. The other type of circuit employs an amplifier with no inversion and a tuned circuit with 0° phase shift. We will consider an example of each of these arrangements.

Phase-shift oscillator

This type of oscillator employs a circuit that produces a phase shift of 180°. Consider the simple C-R circuit illustrated in figure 8.1.

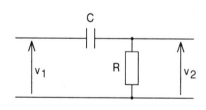   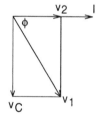

Figure 8.1 *Simple C-R circuit*   **Figure 8.2** *Phasor diagram*

If the phasor diagram for the circuit is examined, see figure 8.2, it can be seen that the amplitude of v_2 is less than that of v_1 and the phase angle of v_2 leads that of v_1 by the angle $\varnothing$, which is between 0° and 90°. However, if more such circuits are combined then a greater phase shift can be achieved. If two C-R circuits are cascaded, as illustrated in figure 8.3, then the phase angle between v_2 and v_1 lies between 0° and 180°.

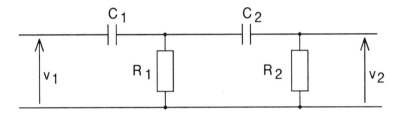

Figure 8.3 *2-pole network*

Clearly, if a phase shift of 180° is required, a further C-R circuit must be used. The circuit shown in figure 8.4 will produce a phase shift between v_1 and v_2 of 180° at *one specific frequency.*

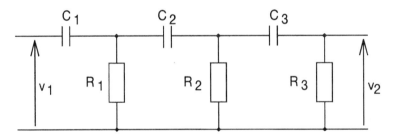

Figure 8.4 *3-pole phase shift circuit*

The expression for that frequency is much simplified if the C-R networks are identical, i.e. $C_1 = C_2 = C_3 = C$ and $R_1 = R_2 = R_3 = R$. The frequency of operation, f_o, is then given by

$$f_o = \frac{1}{2\pi C R \sqrt{6}}$$

At this frequency the circuit exhibits a gain of 1/29, hence the feedback fraction, β, = 1/29.

For this circuit to produce oscillations an amplifier must be employed to take the output voltage v_2 to the same amplitude and phase as the input voltage v_1. If the output of the amplifier is connected to the input of the phase-shift network then an oscillator arrangement is produced. Figure 8.5 illustrates such an arrangement.

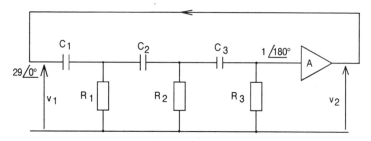

Figure 8.5 *Phase-shift oscillator*

However, this circuit will not oscillate unless the output of the amplifier has the same magnitude and phase as the input of the phase-shift network. The amplifier must, therefore, have a gain of 29 and produce a phase shift between input and output of 180°. The complete circuit will then have a loop gain (gain with feedback) of $1\angle0°$.

The amplifier could be a transistor connected in common-emitter configuration or an inverting op-amp. In either case the input resistance of the amplifier must be taken into consideration as it will change the value of the final resistor in the phase-shift network.

Consider the phase-shift oscillator that employs a common-emitter transistor amplifier, as illustrated in figure 8.6.

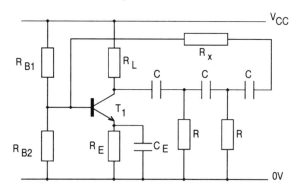

Figure 8.6 *Phase-shift oscillator using BJT*

If a Bipolar Junction Transistor (BJT) is used as the amplifying device the relatively low input impedance of the transistor requires that a series resistor, R_x, be used to couple the phase-shift circuit to the input of the transistor. The combination of resistances, R_x, R_{B1}, R_{B2} and h_{ie1} must provide an overall resistance equal to the network resistance R, such that

$$R = R_x + \left(\frac{1}{\dfrac{1}{R_{B1}} + \dfrac{1}{R_{B2}} + \dfrac{1}{h_{ie1}}} \right)$$

The voltage gain of the amplifier must be 29, as indicated earlier. Recalling work done in chapter 1, $A_v = \dfrac{h_{fe} R_L}{h_{ie}}$. Clearly the value of R_L will be the main method of determining the gain of the amplifier. However, to compensate for changes in h_{fe} and h_{ie} of T_1, the value of R_L must be variable. But R_L is connected across the phase-shift network and if its value is changed then the frequency of operation will be altered. Therefore the value of R_L has a direct effect upon the frequency at which this circuit oscillates, the expression changing to

$$f_o = \frac{1}{2 \pi R C \sqrt{6 + \dfrac{4 R_L}{R}}}$$

If an inverting op-amp is employed as the amplifier similar problems occur with regard to the input resistance of the amplifier. Consider the circuit shown in figure 8.7. The input resistor R_{in} is effectively shunting the final resistor in the phase-shift network, changing its value. The result of this would be that the oscillator would not work at the frequency that was intended.

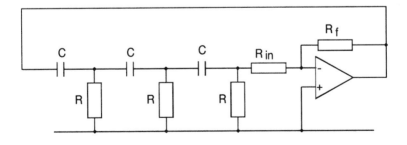

Figure 8.7 R_{in} *shunts final R*

One simple cure for this problem is to remove the last resistor in the network and make R_{in} of the amplifier the same value as R. The feedback resistor, R_f would then be adjusted to achieve the required gain of 29, i.e.

$$R_f = 29 \times R$$

The circuit is illustrated in figure 8.8.

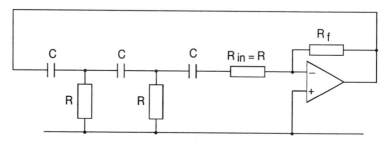

Figure 8.8 *Corrected circuit*

As with the transistor amplifier it is usual to have the gain of the amplifier variable. However, to compensate for any changes in amplifier gain due to temperature variation, the feedback resistance may be a combination of variable resistor and NTC (Negative Temperature Coefficient) thermistor. Any change in the gain of the amplifier would produce a change in current flowing in the feedback resistances. This, in turn, would produce a change in the value of the thermistor which, with a correctly-selected thermistor value, would counter the original change, producing equilibrium.

A typical circuit arrangement is shown in figure 8.9.

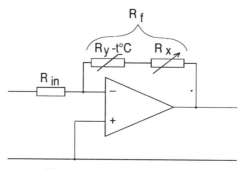

Figure 8.9 *Stabilisation circuit*

Example of circuit operation

If the gain of the amplifier were to increase, the current through R_f would increase and the temperature of the thermistor would also increase. The value of the thermistor, and therefore R_f overall, would fall and the gain of the amplifier would be reduced, compensating for the original increase.

Note that any change in R_{in} is undesirable as it would affect both gain and frequency of operation.

Variable frequency operation

To obtain variable frequency operation all resistors or all capacitors must have their values changed simultaneously. In the case of the transistor amplifier it is not possible to vary the resistance values as one of the Rs is derived from the input resistance of the amplifier. If the capacitors are to be adjusted then a ganged arrangement is required. However, ganged capacitors are usually constructed with one plate of the capacitors commoned, an arrangement that is not practical for the circuits as shown. It is possible, however, to interpose the Cs and Rs of the phase-shift network, producing a circuit in which the capacitors are arranged with one terminal connected to ground, see figure 8.10.

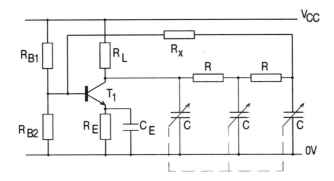

Figure 8.10 *Variable frequency circuit (BJT)*

In the case of the operational amplifier circuit the resistors can be made variable if a buffer amplifier is included in the circuit. The diagram in figure 8.11 illustrates the arrangement in which a non-inverting buffer is inserted between the phase shift network and the inverting amplifier.

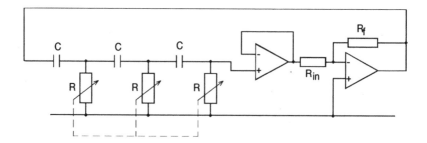

Figure 8.11 *Variable frequency circuit (op-amp)*

The op-amp circuit could be considerably cheaper than that employing expensive ganged capacitors as ganged potentiometers tend to be cheaper than capacitors and, in addition, many op-amp i.c. packages contain two amplifiers.

The two phase-shift oscillator circuits described are not suitable for high frequency operation because the input capacitance of the amplifier adversely affects the frequency of operation at high frequencies, causing oscillation to occur at a frequency other than that designed for.

Example 8.1

Design an oscillator, using a 3-element R-C circuit, for operation at 10 kHz. Let C = 10 nF.

$$R = \frac{1}{2 \pi C f_0 \sqrt{6}}$$

$$R = \frac{1}{2 \pi \times 10 \times 10^{-9} \times 10 \times 10^{3} \sqrt{6}}$$

$$\underline{R = 650 \, \Omega}$$

$$\underline{R_f = 29 \times R = 18.85 \, k\Omega}$$

8.1.2 Wien network oscillator

The Wien network is employed in many frequency-conscious circuits, for example filters and oscillators. The Wien network (or bridge) produces a phase shift of 0° at one particular frequency, making it suitable for a sine wave oscillator. Clearly, if the network produces a phase-shift of 0° the amplifier must do the same and a non-inverting op-amp is ideal for this purpose. The Wien network comprises two capacitors and two resistors and, if $R_1 = R_2 = R$ and $C_1 = C_2 = C$, the frequency at which zero phase shift occurs may be expressed as

$$f_o = \frac{1}{2 \pi R C}$$

At the frequency of operation, the network exhibits a gain of $\frac{1}{3} \angle 0°$.

To obtain oscillation, v_2 must be made to equal v_1, in terms of phase and amplitude. A non-inverting amplifier with a gain of 3 must be used. If the output of the amplifier is connected to the input of the Wien network a sine wave oscillator is produced, see figure 8.12.

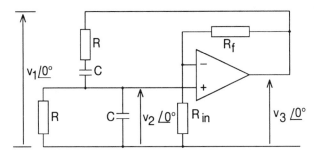

Figure 8.12 *Wien network oscillator*

As the expression for the gain of a non-inverting op-amp is

$$A_v = 1 + \frac{R_f}{R_{in}}$$

and A_v must equal 3, it follows that

$$\boxed{\frac{R_f}{R_{in}} = 2}$$

The Wien network oscillator suffers the same problems of component drift with age and temperature as the phase-shift oscillator described earlier. Similar solutions, for example the thermistor circuit illustrated in figure 8.9, may be used in order to overcome the problem.

Variable frequency operation is more easily achieved than with the previous circuit, by the use of ganged capacitors or ganged resistors.

Example 8.2

Calculate the value of R in a Wien network oscillator in order to obtain $f_o = 10$ kHz. Let $R_{in} = 10$ kΩ and $C = 10$ nF, then $R_f = 20$ kΩ and

$$R = \frac{1}{2\pi \times 10 \times 10^{-9} \times 10 \times 10^3} = \underline{\mathbf{1.59 \text{ k}\Omega}}$$

8.1.2 L-C oscillators

A basic tuned-circuit oscillator

For high frequency sine wave oscillation an L-C tuned circuit is employed. In the simple circuit illustrated in figure 8.13, the tuned circuit is the collector load of the transistor.

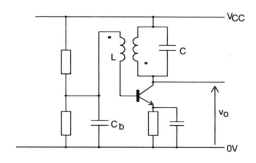

Figure 8.13 *Tuned-circuit oscillator*

Note the presence in the circuit of figure 8.13 of the capacitor C_b, employed to de-couple the ground end of the base winding of L. This is required in order to develop the whole of the feedback signal across the winding of the transformer and ensure maximum signal transfer.

At the frequency of operation, f_o, the gain of the circuit is at its highest (refer to the response of the tuned-circuit amplifier described in chapter 2). The 360° loop phase required for oscillation is provided by the transistor, 180°, and the transformer L, a further 180° (note the phase relationship of the transformer windings - indicated by the dots). The frequency of oscillation of this circuit is given, approximately, by

$$f_o \approx \frac{1}{2\pi\sqrt{LC}}$$

Tuning of the oscillator frequency can be achieved by adjusting the value of C or L.

The turns ratio of the transformer, n, is related to the current gain of the transistor such that

$$n = \frac{1}{h_{fe}}$$

The loop gain is given by

$$A_f = h_{fe}\, n$$

In order for oscillations to begin the loop gain must be unity. However, if the loop gain exceeds unity then non-linearities in the transistor characteristics will limit the amplitude of oscillations. Any harmonic distortion introduced as a result will tend to be eliminated by the collector tuned circuit. Two further high frequency sine wave oscillator circuits, Colpitts and Hartley, will be shown, but not analysed, in this book, their relevance to this level of work being rather limited. The design principles for each are similar in that both employ three reactive elements, Colpitts using two capacitors and one inductor and Hartley employing two inductors and one capacitor. The general arrangements of these components are shown in figure 8.14.

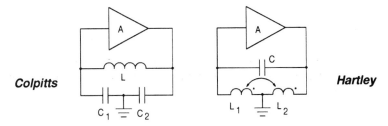

Figure 8.14 *Basic feedback arrangements*

Note that the circuit arrangements illustrated in figure 8.14 require a 180° phase shift from the amplifier.

The Colpitts oscillator

This design, an example of which is shown in figure 8.15, oscillates at a frequency approximating to

$$f_o = \frac{1}{2\pi\sqrt{L\left(\dfrac{C_1 C_2}{C_1 + C_2}\right)}}$$

With reference to the circuit of figure 8.15, the feedback path from collector to base is from the inductor L, through the power supply and the high capacitance, and therefore, low reactance, of C_3.

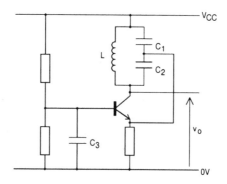

Figure 8.15 *A version of Colpitts oscillator*

The Hartley oscillator

As with the Colpitts oscillator there are many circuit arrangements that meet the requirements of the Hartley oscillator. In the example shown in figure 8.16, the centre of the inductor is connected to signal ground via the power supply. C_c is not part of the tuned circuit, serving only to couple the signal back to the base of the transistor. Frequency of oscillation is given by

$$f_o \approx \frac{1}{2\pi\sqrt{C(L_1 + L_2)}}$$

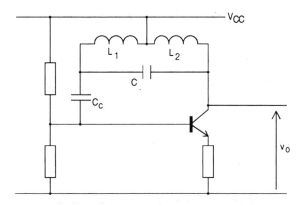

Figure 8.16 *A basic Hartley oscillator*

8.2 Rectangular waveform generators

Most rectangular (or 'square') wave generators derive their output wave-form by saturating an amplifier, usually an op-amp or a transistor circuit. As seen from work at lower levels one popular 'family' of such generators comes under the generic name 'multivibrator'. These include the astable, monostable and bistable circuit arrangements. At lower levels the transistor circuits for each of these multivibrators is introduced and explained and will not, therefore, be repeated here.

This book will limit its investigation of multivibrators to astable circuits, concentrating on circuits that employ logic gates or operational amplifiers.

The astable is a multivibrator with no stable states, i.e. it is a free-running rectangular waveform generator, often used to provide 'clock' signals for digital or microelectronic circuits.

8.2.1 The logic gate astable

The logic gate astable is capable of operating at very high frequencies and may be quartz crystal-controlled for frequency stability. The circuit shown in figure 8.17 employs CMOS inverters.

The operation of the circuit can best be explained by examination of the time-related waveforms for V_{o1}, V_{o2} and V_{i1}. These are illustrated in figure

8.18. V_{SS} is the supply voltage and V_t is the input threshold voltage of the 4069 logic gate.

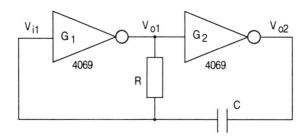

Figure 8.17 *CMOS Logic gate astable*

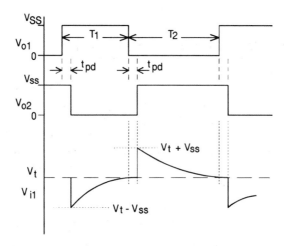

Figure 8.18 *Astable timing waveforms*

Suppose that the sequence commences with C discharged and V_{o1} rising from 0 V to V_{SS}. After the propagation delay t_{pd} of G_2, V_{o2} falls and V_{i1} falls by the same amount, V_{SS}. If it is assumed that V_{i1} was originally at the threshold voltage, V_t, it will now be at $V_t - V_{SS}$. C will now begin to charge towards V_{SS}, reducing the current in R. The charging period, T_1 is terminated when $V_{i1} = V_t$ and may be determined by resolving the charging equation

$$V_{i1} = (V_t - V_{SS}) + (2V_{SS} - V_t)(1 - e^{-\frac{t}{CR}})$$

Commence by removing all brackets

$$V_{i1} = V_t - V_{SS} + 2V_{SS} - 2V_{SS}\, e^{-\frac{t}{CR}} - V_t + V_t\, e^{-\frac{t}{CR}}$$

But $V_{i1} = V_t$ and $-V_{SS} + 2V_{SS} = V_{SS}$, therefore

$$V_t = V_t + V_{SS} - 2V_{SS}\, e^{-\frac{t}{CR}} - V_t + V_t\, e^{-\frac{t}{CR}}$$

$$2V_{SS}\, e^{-\frac{t}{CR}} - V_t\, e^{-\frac{t}{CR}} = V_{SS} - V_t$$

$$e^{-\frac{t}{CR}}\, (\, 2V_{SS} - V_t\,) = V_{SS} - V_t$$

$$e^{-\frac{t}{CR}} = \frac{V_{SS} - V_t}{2V_{SS} - V_t}$$

taking the natural log of each side produces

$$-\frac{t}{CR} = \log_e \left(\frac{V_{SS} - V_t}{2V_{SS} - V_t} \right)$$

$$t = -CR \log_e \left(\frac{V_{SS} - V_t}{2V_{SS} - V_t} \right)$$

the minus sign may be taken inside the log expression as follows

$$t = CR \log_e \left(\frac{V_{SS} - V_t}{2V_{SS} - V_t} \right)^{-1}$$

$T_1 = t$, therefore

$$\boxed{T_1 = CR \log_e \left(\frac{2V_{SS} - V_t}{V_{SS} - V_t} \right)}$$

When V_{i1} reaches V_t, the gate, G_1, turns ON and after its propagation delay, t_{pd}, its output, V_{o1}, falls to 0 V. After a further propagation delay V_{o2} rises to V_{SS} and the capacitor begins to discharge, having initially jumped from V_t to $V_t + V_{SS}$. The equation for the discharge of C is as follows

$$V_{i1} = (\, V_{SS} + V_t\,)\, e^{-\frac{t}{CR}}$$

which, after a similar process to that carried out for T_1 produces

$$T_2 = CR \log_e \left(\frac{V_{SS} + V_t}{V_t} \right)$$

The frequency of oscillation of this circuit is given by

$$f_o = \frac{1}{T_1 + T_2}$$

8.2.2 An op-amp astable

Figure 8.19 shows the circuit diagram of an op-amp astable.

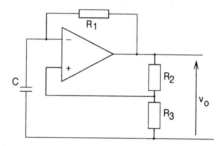

Figure 8.19 *An op-amp astable circuit*

The periodic time of the op-amp astable is given by

$$T_p = 2 C R_1 \log_e \left(1 + \frac{2 R_3}{R_2} \right)$$

However, the expression for frequency of oscillation can be simplified if R_2 is selected to be $1.164 R_3$. Then

$$f_o = \frac{1}{2 C R_1}$$

8.3 Triangular waveform generators

The most popular of these generators employs an op-amp integrator, as described in chapter 6. When used in conjunction with a voltage comparator a circuit is produced that generates both rectangular and triangular waves. Consider the circuit illustrated in figure 8.20. The output of the voltage comparator is used to drive the input of the integrator and the output of the integrator is fed back to switch the comparator. This circuit forms the basis of a simple function generator.

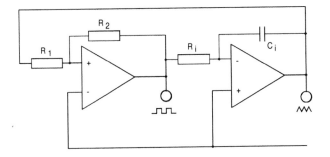

Figure 8.20 *Simple function generator*

The output waveforms of the circuit of figure 8.20 are illustrated in figure 8.21. Note that, as indicated in chapter 6, the output of the integrator is falling when the output of the comparator is high.

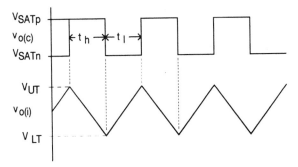

Figure 8.21 *Output waveforms*

In order to determine the frequency of operation of the circuit shown in figure 8.20 the periodic time must be calculated. As the output voltage of the integrator is the input to the comparator it is essential to obtain a value for V_{UT} and V_{LT} for the comparator before attempting to calculate the periodic time of the generator. Consider example 8.3.

Example 8.3

If, for a comparator/integrator circuit as shown in figure 8.20, $V_{SATp} = +12\ V$, $V_{SATn} = -12\ V$, $V_{ref} = 0\ V$, $R_1 = 10\ k\Omega$, $R_2 = 20\ k\Omega$, $R_i = 5\ k\Omega$ and $C_i = 10\ nF$, calculate the frequency of oscillation.

$$V_{UT} = \frac{-V_{SATn}\,R_1}{R_2}$$

$$V_{UT} = \frac{12 \times 10 \times 120^3}{20 \times 10^3}$$

$$\underline{\boldsymbol{V_{UT} = +6\ V}}$$

$$V_{LT} = \frac{-V_{SATp}\,R_1}{R_2}$$

$$V_{LT} = \frac{-12 \times 10 \times 10^3}{20 \times 10^3}$$

$$\underline{\boldsymbol{V_{LT} = -6\ V}}$$

The output of the integrator is V_{UT} - V_{LT}, i.e.

$$V_{UT} - V_{LT} = +6 - (-6) = +12\ V$$

*The input to the integrator is **either** V_{SATp} or V_{SATn}, therefore*

$$t_h = \frac{V_o\,C\,R}{V_{in}} = \frac{12 \times 10 \times 10^{-9} \times 5 \times 10^3}{12}$$

$$\underline{\boldsymbol{t_h = 50\ \mu s}}$$

As V_{SATp} and V_{SATn} have the same magnitude, t_l will be equal to t_h and, therefore, the periodic time will be 100 µs. The frequency will then be the reciprocal of the periodic time, i.e.

$$f_0 = \frac{1}{100 \times 10^{-6}} = \underline{\textbf{10 kHz.}}$$

8.4 Sine wave synthesis

A practical function generator will have a sine wave output in addition to the rectangular and triangular waveforms described. This option may be generated by one of the means described earlier, i.e. a true sine wave with no harmonic content. However, it is possible for the sine wave output to be synthesised from the triangular waveform. If the slope of a triangular wave is changed several times over the period of a quarter cycle, it can be made to appear to be a sine wave. Figure 8.22 illustrates the effect of suitable adjustment of the slope of a triangular wave.

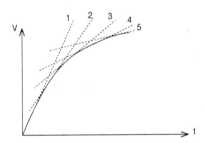

Figure 8.22 *5 changes of slope*

Consider a simple inverting op-amp. If a triangular waveform is applied at its input an inverted and amplified triangular waveform appears at its output. The slope of that output waveform depends upon three variable quantities

- ☐ the amplitude of the input signal
- ☐ the frequency of the input signal
- ☐ the voltage gain of the amplifier

Assuming that the input signal remains unchanged, the remaining variable quantity is the gain of the amplifier. It follows, therefore, that the slope of the output can be controlled directly by adjusting the gain of the amplifier.

It can be proved quite easily that the slope of the output waveform is directly proportional to the gain of the amplifier. As the gain is reduced, so is the slope of the triangular waveform. Of course, any change in gain must take place automatically at various points on the output waveform. This switching can be achieved by altering the value of the feedback resistor, R_f, by adding resistance in parallel with R_f. Consider the circuit of figure 8.23.

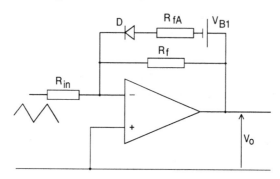

Figure 8.23 *Circuit for automatic slope change*

The potential V_{B1} biases the diode D off when the output voltage is less than V_{B1}. When the output rises above that potential, the diode conducts and effectively connects R_{fA} in parallel with R_f, reducing the effective feedback resistance. As a result, the gain of the amplifier and the slope of the output waveform will be lowered, as illustrated in figure 8.24.

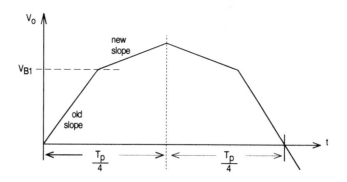

Figure 8.24 *Slope changed at break point*

A more practical means of producing a break voltage is illustrated in figure 8.25.

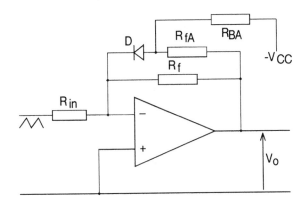

Figure 8.25 *Alternative single-break circuit*

The break potential is now derived from the supply $-V_{CC}$ and the potential divider circuit of R_{fA} and R_{BA} such that

$$V_{B1} = -V_{CC}\frac{R_{fA}}{R_{BA}}$$

In addition, the new slope produced by the break is

$$\text{new slope} = \text{old slope} \times \frac{R_f \mathbin{/\mkern-5mu/} R_{fA}}{R_f}$$

Of course, in practice, many more break points are required in order to produce a viable synthesised sine wave. In addition, it should be noted that the circuits illustrated in figures 8.25 and 8.23 provide for breaks in the positive half-cycles of the output signal only. Additional circuits would be required to provide break points in the negative half-cycle.

A circuit that provides three break points in each half-cycle is shown in figure 8.26.

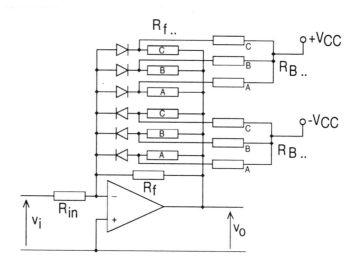

Figure 8.26 *Multiple break sine wave synthesiser*

Many modern waveform generators are programmable, i.e. the shape of the output waveform can be preselected or programmed by the engineer/technician using the equipment. This feature is achieved by the use of high-speed digital and microprocessor-controlled circuits. The shape of the waveform is digitised and stored in memory devices under microprocessor control. It is then read from memory in digital form and converted into a suitable analogue output signal by high-speed Digital to Analogue converters. Filter circuits may then be employed to remove unwanted harmonic signals.

9 Filters

A filter is an electronic circuit that prevents the passage of signals, in a certain band of frequencies, from one circuit to another. There are four types of filter associated with the frequency band in which they operate. These are

- [ ] low pass
- [ ] high pass
- [ ] band pass
- [ ] band stop

Each filter has an ideal characteristic that cannot be achieved practically. In efforts to attain a response close to ideal, several response shapes have been obtained by experiment and have become accepted as standards. Some of these will be examined later in this chapter.

There are also two categories of filter that describe the presence, or otherwise, of active components, i.e. circuits with or without amplification. The *passive* filter is achieved by employing a combination of capacitors, inductors and resistors. *Active* filters use amplifiers, mostly op-amps, and capacitors and resistors in order to produce standard response curves.

This chapter will introduce the concepts of filters and indicate the ideal characteristics for the four types listed above. It will also illustrate the main differences in the shape of the standard response curves. Finally, it will concentrate upon a range of active filters that produce one of the standard responses for low and high pass operation.

9.1 Filter characteristics

9.1.1 Ideal characteristics

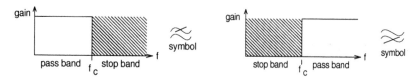

Figure 9.1 *Ideal low pass response*   **Figure 9.2** *Ideal high pass response*

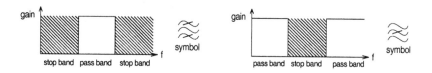

Figure 9.3 *Ideal band pass response*   **Figure 9.4** *Ideal band stop response*

The cut-off frequency, f_c, is the point at which the filter response changes from pass band to stop band. In practical filters the change from pass band to stop band is a gradual process, the slope of the 'roll-off' being a function of the filter characteristic. For practical filters f_c is the frequency at which the response is 3 dB down on the reference level.

9.1.2 Practical filter response

In practice the response of a filter consists of a relatively flat area in the pass band, a 'knee' area in which the filter response begins to roll off and the roll-off itself in which a linear slope is achieved. The bandwidth of the filter is described by that area of the pass band in which the output is greater than 0.707 of the reference level.

The rate at which a filter response rolls off is set by the 'order' or 'degree' of the filter; for example a 1st order filter response rolls off at 20 dB/decade, 2nd order at 40 dB/decade, 3rd order at 60 dB/decade, etc. A practical low pass filter response would be as shown in figure 9.5.

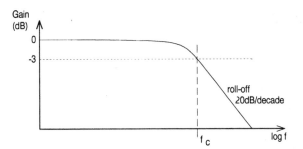

Figure 9.5 *Practical low pass filter response*

9.1.3 Standard filter responses

Filter responses may be described in terms of the transfer function, for example, Butterworth, Chebyshev, Bessel and Cauer. Each filter has features that make it especially useful in certain applications.

It should be noted that most filter designs suffer from the presence of an unwanted output at some frequencies in the stop band. However, this can generally be removed by suitable attenuation of the filter output signal.

The Butterworth response

The responses of Butterworth filters are, for the most part, flat in the pass band although they tend to start their roll-off fairly gently. The higher the order or degree of the filter, the steeper the roll-off and the closer is the response to the ideal, seen earlier.

The Chebyshev response

This is similar to that of the Butterworth filter except that, in order to achieve a sharper 'knee', there is a degree of rippling in the pass band.

The Cauer response

This response provides for a very high impedance at the cut-off frequency, but with a higher output at frequencies in the stop band than the Butterworth and Chebyshev responses.

The Bessel response

In most analogue applications the phase shift experienced by signals as they pass through the filter is not important, hence little attention is paid to that aspect. However, if digital signals are to be filtered, phase differences take on considerable significance.

The other filters mentioned, Butterworth, Chebyshev and Cauer all introduce phase changes around the cut-off frequency. The Bessel response, however, is designed to produce linear phase shift over the whole of the pass band.

Figure 9.6 shows the 'knee' for low pass filters with the responses discussed.

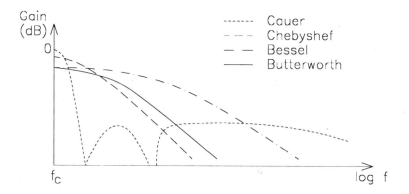

Figure 9.6 *A comparison of response 'knees'*

Having outlined, albeit briefly, the differences between the standard filter responses it can be stated that, for most purposes, a Butterworth response is considered perfectly suitable and, consequently, will be the only response dealt with in the rest of this chapter.

9.2 Active filters

Passive filters would normally require the inclusion of some inductance in order to achieve high roll-off rates. This would present the filter designer with the following problems attendant with the use of inductors

- relatively expensive
- bulky at low frequencies
- emission of electromagnetic radiation

However, by employing active filters, good roll-off rates can be obtained with simple R-C circuits. In addition, the active filter, employing some form of amplifier, acts as a buffer between the filter circuit and any load placed upon it and can be configured to provide voltage gain in the pass band. Our discussion will be limited to active filters that employ operational amplifiers, as these are most widely used nowadays.

9.2.1 Low pass filters

1st order Butterworth response

The first order active filter is obtained by connecting a voltage follower to the output of a passive R-C filter, as illustrated in figure 9.7.

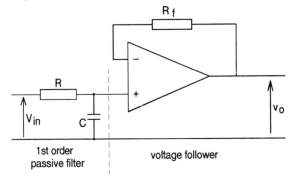

Figure 9.7 *1st order low pass filter*

The reactance of C is very high at low frequencies, having negligible effect on the applied signal. However, as the frequency of that signal increases the reactance of C falls, shunting the signal and reducing the amplitude of the signal applied to the non-inverting terminal of the op-amp.

To provide equal d.c. resistance paths for both input terminals, R_f is made equal to R. As indicated earlier in this chapter, the roll-off rate for this order of filter is 20 dB/decade, as shown in figure 9.8.

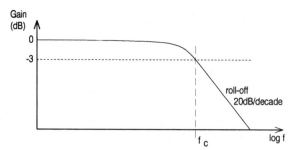

Figure 9.8 *Low pass filter response*

Note that the response of this filter circuit is identical to that of the high frequency circuit for cascaded R-C coupled amplifier stages - hence the same rate of roll-off.

The gain of the voltage follower is, of course, unity. Therefore v_o may be assumed to be developed across the reactance of the capacitor, C. With v_{in} connected across R and X_C in series, the output voltage is v_{in} multiplied by the ratio of X_C to $R + X_C$. The derivation of cut-off frequency commences at this point, hence

$$v_o = v_{in} \frac{\dfrac{1}{j\omega C}}{R + \dfrac{1}{j\omega C}}$$

multiplying top and bottom by $j\omega C$ gives

$$v_o = v_{in} \frac{\dfrac{j\omega C}{j\omega C}}{j\omega C R + \dfrac{j\omega C}{j\omega C}}$$

$$v_o = \frac{v_{in}}{1 + j\omega C R}$$

For our purposes we can neglect the phase angle of this complex expression so that the magnitude of v_o is

$$|v_o| = \frac{v_{in}}{1 + \omega C R}$$

and, therefore, voltage gain

$$\frac{V_o}{V_{in}} = \frac{1}{1 + \omega C R}$$

At f_c, $\frac{V_o}{V_{in}} = 0.707$ or $\frac{1}{\sqrt{2}}$ so

$$\frac{1}{\sqrt{2}} = \frac{1}{1 + \omega_c C R}$$

$$\sqrt{2} = 1 + \omega_c C R$$

squaring both sides

$$2 = 1^2 + \omega_c^2 C^2 R^2$$

$$2 = 1 + \omega_c^2 C^2 R^2$$

$$\omega_c^2 C^2 R^2 = 1$$

$$\omega_c C R = 1$$

$$\omega_c = \frac{1}{C R}$$

$$f_c = \frac{1}{2 \pi C R}$$

Note that, in many cases, both C and R will be unknown and the designer will have to select a suitable value for one of the components and calculate the value of the other. It would, in general, be inappropriate to select either very high or very low values for R or C.

Example 9.1

Design a 1st order low pass filter with a Butterworth response and a cut-off frequency of 20 kHz.

As two resistors (R and R_f) must have the same value, select a value for R, between 1 kΩ and 10 kΩ.

Let R = 10 kΩ.

$$C = \frac{1}{2\pi f_c R}$$

$$C = \frac{1}{2\pi\, 20 \times 10^3 \times 10 \times 10^3} = \underline{796\ pF}$$

2nd order Butterworth response

Sallen and Key developed two second order filter arrangements which employ special circuitry to produce either

- ☐ unity gain or
- ☐ equal component filters.

In order to produce these conditions, a very strict relationship between component values has to be observed. Figure 9.9 shows a unity gain filter in which, under certain circumstances, R_f could be replaced with a link.

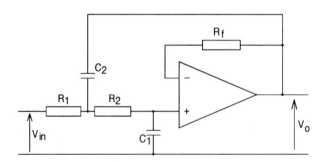

Figure 9.9 *Sallen and Key 2nd order low pass filter*

In this circuit arrangement, $R_1 = R_2 = R$ and $R_f = 2R$, a suitable value for R generally being selected, for example, 10 kΩ. The value of the capacitors can then be obtained from

$$C_1 = \frac{0.707}{2\pi f_c R} \quad \text{and} \quad C_2 = 2\,C_1$$

The frequency response curve for this filter is as shown in figure 9.10.

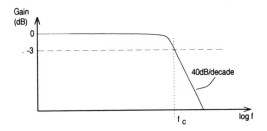

Figure 9.10 *2nd order low pass filter response*

Example 9.2

If R is selected to be 10 kΩ, calculate the values of C_1 and C_2 for a low pass filter with a cut-off frequency of 20 kHz.

$$C_1 = \frac{0.707}{2\pi f_c R} = \frac{0.707}{2\pi \times 20 \times 10^3 \times 10 \times 10^3}$$

$$\underline{C_1 = 563\,pF}$$

$$C_2 = 2\,C_1 = \underline{1.126\,nF}$$

3rd order Butterworth response

A third order filter is obtained by cascading a first order filter and a second order filter as illustrated in figure 9.11.

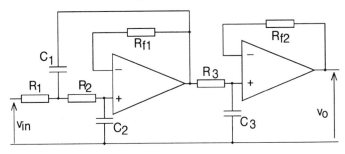

Figure 9.11 *3rd order low pass filter*

Again, this circuit produces a gain of unity, with a roll-off rate of 60 dB/decade. $R_1 = R_2 = R_3 = R$, usually selected by the filter designer. $R_{f1} = 2R$ and $R_{f2} = R$. Capacitances are calculated as follows

$$C_3 = \frac{1}{2 \pi f_c R}, \quad C_2 = \frac{C_3}{2} \text{ and } C_1 = 2C_3$$

9.2.2 High pass filters

High pass filters are obtained by interposing the capacitors and resistors in the low pass filter circuits illustrated earlier. The Sallen and Key 2nd order high pass filter circuit employs equal value capacitors and, therefore, selection of the capacitance value and calculation of suitable resistor values is recommended for high pass filters.

1st order Butterworth filter

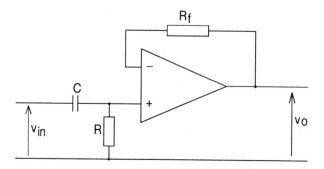

Figure 9.12 *1st order high pass filter*

The reactance of C, in figure 9.12, is very high at low frequencies, providing a high resistance to such signals. As the frequency of the applied signal increases, so the reactance of C decreases, allowing more of the signal to appear at the output.

As for the first order low pass filter, the expression for cut-off frequency is

$$f_c = \frac{1}{2 \pi C R}$$

As shown in figure 9.13, the low frequency roll-off takes place at 20 dB/decade.

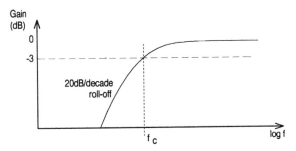

Figure 9.13 *1st order high pass filter response*

Again, R_f is made equal to R, to provide equal resistance paths for both op-amp input terminals.

Example 9.3

If C is selected to be 10 nF, calculate the values of R and R_f for a 1st order high-pass filter with $f_c = 1$ kHz.

$$R = R_f = \frac{1}{2 \pi f_c C}$$

$$R = R_f = \frac{1}{2 \pi \times 1 \times 10^3 \times 10 \times 10^{-9}}$$

$$\underline{R = R_f = 15.92 \ k\Omega}$$

2nd order Butterworth filter

As indicated, $C_1 = C_2 = C$. Resistances are then calculated from

$$R_1 = \frac{1.414}{2 \pi f_c C}, \quad R_2 = \frac{R_1}{2} \quad \text{and} \quad R_{f1} = R_1$$

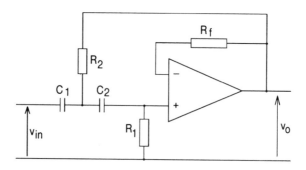

Figure 9.14 *2nd order high pass filter*

Example 9.4

Design a 2nd order high pass filter with a cut-off frequency of 1 kHz.

Select a value for C of 10 nF. Then

$$R_1 = \frac{1.414}{2\pi f_c C}$$

$$R_1 = \frac{1.414}{2\pi \times 1 \times 10^3 \times 10 \times 10^{-9}}$$

$$\underline{R_1 = 22.50\ k\Omega}$$

$$\underline{R_f = 22.50\ k\Omega\ :\ R_2 = 11.25\ k\Omega}$$

3rd order Butterworth filter

As with the third order low pass filter, this degree of filter is achieved by cascading a second order and a first order filter, as shown in figure 9.15.

For this filter $C_1 = C_2 = C_3 = C$, the value of which is selected. The values of R_1, R_2, R_3, R_{f1} and R_{f2} are then determined as follows

$$R_3 = \frac{1}{2 \pi f_c C} \qquad R_1 = 2 R_3 \qquad R_2 = \frac{R_3}{2}$$

$$R_{f1} = R_1 \qquad R_{f2} = R_3$$

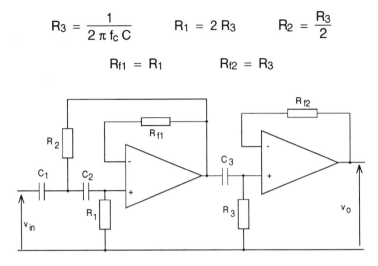

Figure 9.15 *3rd order high pass filter*

9.2.3 Band pass and band stop filters

Band pass or band stop filters can be achieved by cascading or paralleling low pass and high pass filters with suitable cut-off frequencies. A band pass filter would require that the low and high pass filters were in cascade, whereas the band stop filter would need the filters to be in parallel.

Band pass filter

Consider the circuit shown in figure 9.16.

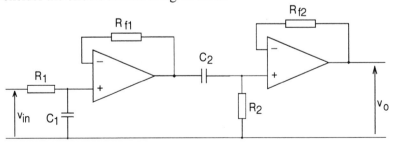

Figure 9.16 *Cascaded high and low pass filters*

If the low pass filter ($f_c = 1/2\pi C_1 R_1$) had a cut-off frequency of, say, 10 kHz and the high pass filter ($fc = 1/2\pi C2R2$) had a cut-off frequency of, say, 9 kHz then a narrow band of frequencies between 9 and 10 kHz would be allowed to pass and all others would be rejected. The frequency response of a first order band pass filter is illustrated in figure 9.17.

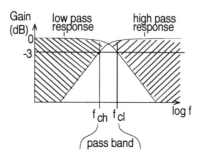

Figure 9.17 *Band pass filter response*

Band stop filter

A band stop filter can be obtained by connecting a low pass filter in parallel (shunt) with a high pass filter, see figure 9.18 (the buffers are present to prevent the output stage of one filter from shunting signals from the other).

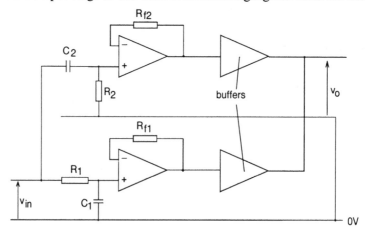

Figure 9.18 *Low and high pass filters in shunt*

The cut-off frequency of the high pass filter would be higher than that of the low pass filter, resulting in the response illustrated in figure 9.19.

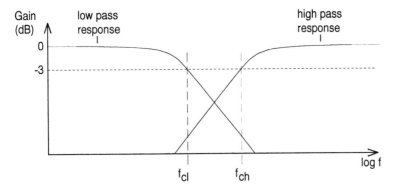

Figure 9.19 *Band stop filter response*

In practice, band pass or band stop ('notch') filters are likely to require a higher Q than that available from the circuit of figure 9.18. The use of a twin-tee or 'bridged tee' circuit allows for higher values of Q, providing much narrower, and therefore more frequency-selective, notches. Figure 9.20 shows a typical twin-tee notch filter.

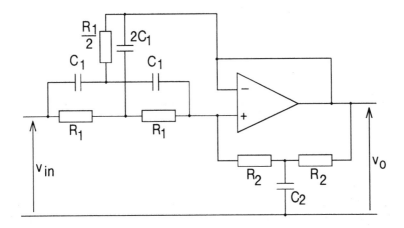

Figure 9.18 *Twin-tee notch filter*

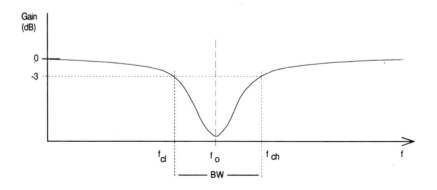

Figure 9.21 Notch filter response

For the circuit illustrated in figure 9.20, the frequency of operation (that is, the frequency midway between the upper and lower cut-off frequencies) is given by

$$f_o = \frac{1}{2 \pi R_1 C_1}$$

and the Q of the circuit is given by

$$Q = \frac{R_2}{2 R_1} = \frac{C_1}{C_2}$$

The relationship between f_o and Q remains as stated for the tuned-collector amplifier (see chapter 2 - Small Signal Amplifiers),

$$Q = \frac{f_o}{BW}$$

It should be noted that the twin-tee circuit will not reject harmonics of its frequency of operation. For this reason the circuit is often used in instrumentation for detecting the presence and magnitude of harmonic distortion.

Example 9.5

Using a twin-tee circuit, design an active filter with a frequency of operation of 1 kHz and a Q of 10.

Let C_1 = 10 nF. Then

$$R_1 = \frac{1}{2 \pi f_0 C_1}$$

$$\boldsymbol{R_1 = 15.92 \, k\Omega}$$

Since Q = 10,

$$R_2 = 20 \, R_1 = \boldsymbol{318.3 \, k\Omega}$$

Finally

$$C_2 = \frac{C_1}{Q} = \frac{10 \times 10^{-9}}{10} = \boldsymbol{1 \, nF}$$

10 Noise

In this chapter, noise will be defined and its types and sources identified. In addition, such terms as signal-to-noise ratio, noise factor (figure), noise temperature, etc. will be explained and evaluated. Particular attention will be paid to noise generated in electronic components, for example passive components such as resistors, and active components such as transistors and operational amplifiers. Electronic or electrical noise may be defined as any unwanted signal which is present in an electrical or electronic system. This unwanted signal is called interference.

10.1 Sources of noise

Noise can be classified as being either interference, i.e. present outside an electronic system, or inherent, that is internal to the circuit. The circuit designer will, in most cases, take steps to minimise the amount of external noise that is received by his circuit, usually by appropriate shielding and earthing. Inherent noise, however, is a function of the components, active and passive, that are employed in the system design. In order to efficiently 'design out' noise it is essential to understand its sources and causes.

The main types of noise are as follows

     □   Resistance noise
     □   Current noise
     □   Bi-polar transistor noise
     □   FET noise

10.1.1 Resistance noise

This is a random noise caused by thermal agitation of electrons in a conductor. When the temperature of a conductor is raised above absolute zero (0° Kelvin or −273°C) its atoms begin to vibrate about their mean positions. This vibration is quite small at room temperatures, but is sufficient to generate a current in the conductor that is random in direction. This current produces a voltage at the terminals of the conductor which, in turn, produces noise. The r.m.s. noise voltage produced by thermal agitation is given by the equation

$$V_n = \sqrt{4\,k\,T\,B\,R}$$

where k = Boltzmann's constant = 1.38×10^{-23} J/°
   T = Temperature of conductor in °K (°K = °C + 273°)
   B = Bandwidth of the circuit at whose output the noise appears
   R = Resistance of circuit or conductor in ohms

Note that it is the bandwidth and temperature, not the frequency of operation, that determine the amount of resistance noise present. Consequently, a wide band amplifier will be noisier than a tuned amplifier, irrespective of its frequency of operation.

Example 10.1

A 4.7 MΩ resistor is operating in an amplifier with a bandwidth of 100 kHz. Calculate the noise voltage generated across the resistor at a temperature of 20 °C.

$$V_n = \sqrt{4 \times 1.38 \times 10^{-23} \times 293 \times 100 \times 10^3 \times 4.7 \times 10^6}$$

$$\underline{\boldsymbol{V_n = 87.19\,\mu V}}$$

10.1.2 Current noise

The noise produced in modern high quality metallic film resistors is that noise described above, i.e. thermal agitation or resistance noise. In the older type of carbon resistor current noise is also produced. Current noise is due to the contact resistance exhibited by particles of carbon when combined to form a resistor. The level of noise increases with both the resistance of the component and the amount of current flowing in it. However, current noise is inversely proportional to frequency. At audio frequencies the current noise in a carbon resistor may be higher than that due to thermal agitation, but at radio frequencies this situation is reversed.

The total noise voltage generated by a carbon resistor is given by

$$V_{n\,(total)} = \sqrt{(\text{thermal noise})^2 + (\text{current noise})^2}$$

10.1.3 Noise in transistors

Thermal agitation noise

Thermal agitation noise is generated by internal resistances within the transistor and, as a result, is present in the base, emitter and collector regions of the transistor. However, the noise generated in the base region is amplified by the transistor and, therefore, presents much more of a problem than in the other two regions.

As previously, the noise voltage produced by thermal agitation is given by

$$V_n = \sqrt{4\,k\,T\,B\,R_b}$$

Shot noise

This is noise generated across a P-N junction by the passage across the junction of small numbers of minority carriers created by thermal agitation. The current created by this movement is independent of the main current flowing across the P-N junction. As bi-polar transistors have two junctions there are two sources of shot noise.

Partition noise

The electrons flowing in the emitter of a transistor divide between its base and collector circuits. Partition noise is produced as a result of random variations in the proportion of current going to the base and collector terminals.

Flicker (1/f) noise

Sometimes called 'pink noise', this is caused by variations in the conductivity of the semiconductor material employed in the construction of the transistor. The level of noise produced is inversely proportional to the frequency of operation. At low frequencies it is greater than shot noise, but at frequencies above 1 kHz it is lower than noise produced elsewhere in the transistor.

10.1.4 Noise in FETs

The FET produces less noise than a bi-polar transistor for the following reasons:
- a FET has only one P-N junction, thereby reducing shot noise by half.
- electrons flowing in the source can only flow into the drain, thereby eliminating partition noise.

10.1.5 Noise in operational amplifiers

Of course, op-amps employ transistors, bi-polar and field effect, and will be subject to the same sources of noise. Clearly, the input stages of an op-amp will be the most crucial in determining the inherent noise produced. Many modern op-amps employ field effect transistors in their input stages in order to keep amplifier noise to a minimum.

Noise specifications for operational amplifiers are not standard, with manufacturers expressing the 'noisiness' of their products in different ways. However, reference to data from *Texas Instruments* and *Maxim* indicates that a method called 'equivalent noise resistance' is employed. This method involves expressing all internally-generated amplifier noise as if it were produced by thermal agitation in an input source resistance. The amplifier is then treated, for analysis, as if it were noiseless.

Hence, a 'low-noise' op-amp may be described as having a noise performance of 4.5 nV/√ Hz max (10 Hz).

Note that Bandwidth has been removed from the expression for thermal agitation noise voltage and a single frequency quoted.

The method of 'equivalent noise resistance' will be examined in greater detail later in this chapter.

10.2 Signal-to-noise ratio

The signal-to-noise ratio of an electronic circuit is defined as the ratio of the signal **power** to the noise **power** at a specific point in the circuit.

$$\text{signal–to–noise ratio} = \frac{S \text{ (signal power)}}{N \text{ (noise power)}}$$

This is normally expressed in dB and is the difference between the signal power (in dB) and the noise power (in dB).

$$\text{S/N ratio} = 10 \log_{10} \frac{S}{N} \text{ dB}$$

$$\text{S/N ratio} = 10 \, (\log_{10} S - \log_{10} N) \text{ dB}$$

$$\text{S/N ratio} = 10 \log_{10} S - 10 \log_{10} N \text{ dB}$$

$$\text{S/N ratio} = S \text{ (dB)} - N \text{ (dB)}$$

In practice the signal-to-noise ratio is expressed in terms of the signal + noise and the noise, such that

$$\text{S/N ratio} = \frac{\text{signal power} + \text{noise power}}{\text{noise power}}$$

Although it is generally quoted in dBs, if signal and noise voltages are quoted the S/N ratio can be expressed as follows

$$\text{S/N ratio} = 20 \log_{10} \frac{V_S}{V_N} \text{ dB}$$

10.3 Equivalent noise resistance

The total noise voltage produced in a transistor, or an op-amp, may, for ease of calculation, be considered to be generated by thermal agitation within a resistance, the value of which is given by the manufacturer of the device. The same is true for the noise current of a transistor. This resistance is called the 'equivalent noise resistance' and values are normally quoted for noise voltage resistance and noise current resistance.

The use of these parameters enables the amplifier to be considered 'noise-less' and the equivalent noise resistances included with any other resistances at the amplifier input. The signal source has a voltage (V_s) and a source resistance (R_s), as illustrated in figure 10.1.

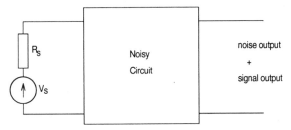

Figure 10.1 *Equivalent circuit*

For the purpose of analysis the source signal is now separated into 'signal' and 'noise' components and amplifier noise separated into noise voltage (V_N) and noise current (I_N).

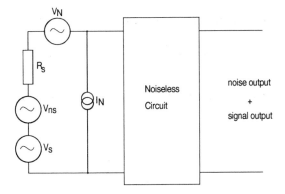

Figure 10.2 *Modified equivalent circuit*

If the noise current is now converted into an equivalent noise voltage (i.e. current through the source resistance) then I_N becomes the voltage $I_N.R_s$ and is in series with all other noise voltages.

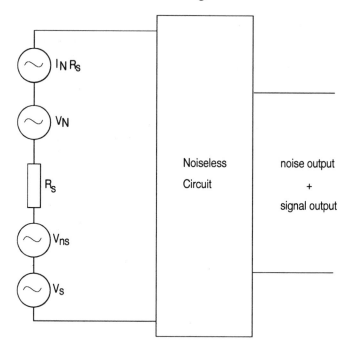

Figure 10.3 *All signals shown as voltages*

The noise voltage (V_N) produced by the equivalent noise resistance (R_{NV}) is derived from

$$V_N = \sqrt{4 \, k \, T_o \, B \, R_{NV}}$$

The noise current (I_N) produced by the equivalent noise resistance (R_{NI}) is derived from

$$I_N = \sqrt{\frac{4 \, k \, T_o \, B}{R_{NI}}}$$

$$I_N \, R_s = \sqrt{\frac{4 \, k \, T_o \, B \, R_s{}^2}{R_{NI}}}$$

Therefore the total noise input voltage to the amplifier is the sum of

- ☐ Thermal noise from source (V_{ns})
- ☐ Noise voltage (V_N)
- ☐ Noise current ($I_N R_s$)

Noise voltages are added by using vector addition (or 'root sum of the squares' addition), so total noise voltage (V_{NT}) is derived as follows

$$V_{NT}^2 = V_{ns}^2 + V_N^2 + (I_N R_S)^2$$

$$V_{NT}^2 = 4 k T_0 B R_S + 4 k T_0 R_{NV} + \frac{4 k T_0 B R_S^2}{R_{NI}}$$

taking out $4kT_0B$ gives

$$V_{NT}^2 = 4 k T_0 B (R_S + R_{NV} + \frac{R_S^2}{R_{NI}})$$

$$\boxed{V_{NT} = \sqrt{4 k T_0 B (R_S + R_{NV} + \frac{R_S^2}{R_{NI}})}}$$

Example 10.2

A transistor, operating at a temperature of 20° C in an amplifier with a bandwidth of 1 MHz, has $R_{NV} = 20\ k\Omega$ and $R_{NI} = 100\ k\Omega$. If the input signal has a source resistance of 10 $k\Omega$, calculate the total noise voltage applied to a 'noiseless' amplifier.

$$V_{NT} = \sqrt{4 k T_0 B (R_S + R_{NV} + \frac{R_S^2}{R_{NI}})}$$

$$V_{NT} = \sqrt{4 \times 1.38 \times 10^{-23}\ 293 \times 10^6 (10^4 + 2 \times 10^4 + \frac{10^8}{10^5})}$$

$$V_{NT} = \sqrt{4 \times 1.38 \times 293 \times 10^{-17} \times 31 \times 10^3}$$

$$\underline{V_{NT} = 22.39\ \mu\ V}$$

10.4 Noise power

The maximum noise power that may be delivered to a load resistance occurs when the load resistance is equal to the resistance of the noise signal source. Figure 10.4 illustrates the arrangement.

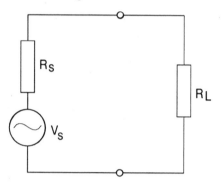

Figure 10.4 *Maximum power transfer occurs when $R_L = R_s$*

Note that as far as the source of noise is concerned, R_L is a load, but it could equally well be the input resistance of a noise-free amplifier or network.

If $R_L = R_s = R$ then the noise voltage across R_L is equal to half V_s, and the noise power in R_L is given by

$$P_{NI} = \frac{(\frac{V_s}{2})^2}{R} \text{ watts}$$

$$P_{NI} = \frac{V_s^2}{4R}$$

As $V_s = \sqrt{4 k T_o B R}$,

$$V_s^2 = 4 k T_o B R$$

therefore

$$P_{NI} = \frac{4 k T_o B R}{4R}$$

and

$$\boxed{P_{NI} = k T_o B \text{ Watts}}$$

If R_L is, in fact, R_{in} of an amplifier with power gain, G, then the noise power at the output of the amplifier will be

$$P_{NO} = G k T_o B \text{ Watts}$$

10.5 Noise factor (F)

The noise signal present at the output of a circuit is a combination of two noise signals, that present at the input of the circuit and that produced by the circuit itself. The measure of the 'noisiness' of a circuit is its noise factor (or noise figure), F. If an amplifier is noise-free, i.e. it does not generate any noise itself, then the signal-to-noise ratio at the output of the amplifier will be the same as at its input.

The signal-to-noise ratio of an amplifier, i.e. its noise factor, may be expressed as follows:

$$F = \frac{\text{Total noise power out } (P_{TO})}{\text{That part of } P_{NO} \text{ due to thermal noise at the input } (P_{NI})}$$

As $P_{NO} = G kT_o B$, where G is the gain of the amplifier

$$F = \frac{P_{TO}}{G k T_o B}$$

$$F = \frac{\dfrac{1}{k T_o B}}{\dfrac{G}{P_{TO}}}$$

multiply top and bottom by P_{SI}

$$F = \frac{\dfrac{P_{SI}}{k T_o B}}{\dfrac{G P_{SI}}{P_{TO}}}$$

As $kT_o B = P_{NI}$ and $G P_{SI} = P_{SO}$

$$F = \cfrac{\cfrac{P_{SI}}{P_{NI}}}{\cfrac{P_{SO}}{P_{TO}}}$$

$$F = \frac{\text{S/N ratio at input}}{\text{S/N ratio at output}}$$

A perfect, noiseless amplifier will have a noise factor of unity, or 0 dB. In practice an amplifier will always generate some noise and therefore the signal-to-noise ratio at its output will always be worse than at its input, making its noise factor greater than 1.

10.5.1 Effective noise figure (F_{eff})

The expression for the noise factor or figure of a circuit assumes that the temperature of the noise source is the same as the temperature of the circuit. However, at times, this will not be true and the expression for F would have to be modified.

To quantify the effective noise figure of an amplifier operating at a temperature other than that of the noise source, it is necessary to produce separate expressions for the output noise due to the input noise and that output noise due to the circuit itself.

Let P_{TO} = TOTAL noise power at the output, P_{NI} = source noise power, P_{NI}' = effective noise input power due to amplifier internal generated noise, P_{TO}' = effective noise output power due to internal generated noise.

P_{TO}' = Total noise power output - Source noise multiplied by amplifier gain, i.e.

$$P_{TO}' = P_{TO} - G\,P_{NI}$$

$$P_{TO}' = F\,G\,k\,T_0\,B - G\,k\,T_0\,B$$

$$P_{TO}' = G\,k\,T_0\,B\,(F-1)$$

and

$$P_{NI}' = \frac{P_{TO}'}{G}$$

$$\boxed{P_{NI}' = k\,T_0\,B\,(F-1)}$$

Let the temperature of the circuit be T_0 and the temperature of the source be T_s. Then, the noise power at the output due to the source noise is

$$P_{NO(s)} = G\,k\,T_s\,B$$

and noise power at output due to the circuit is

$$P_{TO}' = G\,k\,T_0\,B\,(F-1)$$

The effective noise figure, F_{eff}, equals $\dfrac{\text{total noise power at the output}}{\text{noise output due to source noise}}$

$$F_{eff} = \frac{P_{NO(s)} + P_{TO}'}{P_{NO(s)}}$$

$$F_{eff} = \frac{G\,k\,T_s\,B + G\,k\,T_0\,B\,(F-1)}{G\,k\,T_s\,B}$$

$$\boxed{F_{eff} = 1 + \frac{T_0}{T_s}\,(F-1)}$$

11 Power Circuits

This chapter will present and analyse the two main power circuits employed in the field of Analogue Electronics, namely power amplifiers and power supply units. They have been combined into one chapter because of the close relationship between a power amplifier and its power supply.

11.1 Power amplifiers

11.1.1 Class A operation

Although many commercial amplifier designs no longer work in class A, many hi-fi purists consider the sound quality from a class A output stage to be superior to that of classes B or AB. The author is not going to discuss the (perceived) pros and cons of sound purity in relation to amplifier design but does consider it important to discuss and analyse the operation of class A power amplifiers.

The class A amplifier has the major disadvantage that it always draws current from the power supply (half of its maximum under quiescent conditions), making it inefficient and, in the case of power amplifiers, causing it to dissipate large amounts of power (and, therefore, heat). This has led to amplifier designers selecting class B or AB operation - reducing power dissipation and increasing reliability.

The class A power amplifier is similar in configuration to the small signal class A amplifier discussed in chapter 1. However, when matching the output of the amplifier to, say, a loudspeaker, a transformer is likely to be used as an impedance-matching and coupling device.

The voltage gain of power amplifiers tends to be quite low, with devices being selected for their ability to handle large currents. The current gain of a power transistor is also quite low, typically in the order of 20 - 30. The circuit shown in figure 11.1 shows a class A, single-ended, transformer-coupled power amplifier.

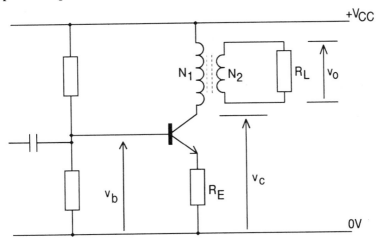

Figure 11.1 *Class A power amplifier*

The circuit arrangement is similar to that for the small signal amplifier discussed in chapter 1. Note, however, that there is no emitter de-coupling capacitor due to the very low value of R_E, typically in the order of < 10 Ω. Note also that phase inversions take place in the transistor and in the transformer, leaving v_o, the signal across R_L, in phase with the applied signal v_b.

As the d.c. resistance of the transformer primary is extremely low, the collector voltage under quiescent (no signal) conditions will be V_{cc}. Note that the biasing conditions on the base of the transistor do not affect the collector quiescent voltage, only the quiescent current. If a positive-going input signal causes maximum collector current to flow, the transistor will be fully conducting and its collector-emitter voltage will be approximately zero. If a negative-going input signal produces maximum collector current in the reverse direction then V_C will attain approximately quiescent voltage + V_{cc}, i.e. the collector voltage will swing between 0 and $2V_{CC}$. Similarly, the maximum change in collector current will be twice it quiescent value, i.e. $2 I_{CQ}$.

The maximum power output from the circuit is the r.m.s. value of V_{CE} multiplied by the r.m.s. value of I_C, i.e.

$$P_{out}max = \frac{V_{cc}}{\sqrt{2}} \frac{I_{CQ}}{\sqrt{2}}$$

$$P_{out}max = \frac{V_{cc} I_{CQ}}{2}$$

The ideal load line for the amplifier, shown in figure 11.2, can be used to represent the load resistance and indicate the quiescent point, d.c. load line and the power dissipation curve.

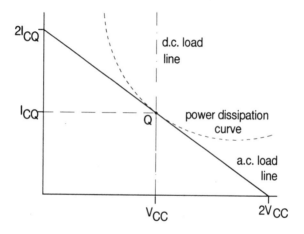

Figure 11.2 *Amplifier characteristic curves*

The power drawn from the power supply is always equal to that at the quiescent point Q, i.e. $V_{cc} I_{CQ}$.

The maximum theoretical power conversion efficiency (PCE) of the class A power amplifier is

$$PCE_{max} = \frac{\text{power supplied to the load}}{\text{power drawn from the supply}}$$

$$PCE_{max} = \frac{\dfrac{V_{cc} I_{CQ}}{2}}{V_{cc} I_{CQ}} \times 100\% = 50\%$$

The calculations assume that the **transformer** is 100% efficient, i.e. the power delivered to R_L is equal to that in the transformer primary. In practice, of course, there will be some losses present in the transformer.

The use of the transformer allows loads with very low impedances to be connected to the amplifier. For example, a loudspeaker with an impedance of, say, 4 Ω could be employed. The turns ratio of the transformer would then be designed to provide a suitable impedance match for the collector load of the transistor.

If the impedance of the transformer primary is R_p, then the turns ratio

$$\frac{N_1}{N_2} = \sqrt{\frac{R_p}{R_L}}$$

Example 11.1

An amplifier is connected to a +12 V supply. If its quiescent collector current is 1 A, calculate the turns ratio of a transformer suitable for driving a 4 Ω loudspeaker to its optimum power output.

The a.c. load line starts at $V_{CE} = 0$, $I_C = 2$ A and terminates at $V_{CE} = 24$ V and $I_C = 0$. The quiescent point, Q is at $I_C = 1$ A, $V_{CE} = 12$ V. The slope of the a.c. load line is $-1/12$. (See figure 11.3 for the characteristic curves.)

$$R_p = \frac{\Delta V_{CE}}{\Delta I_C} = \frac{24}{2} = \underline{12\,\Omega}$$

$$\frac{N_1}{N_2} = \sqrt{\frac{R_p}{R_L}} = \sqrt{3} = \underline{\mathit{1.73}}$$

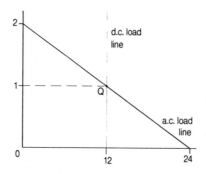

Figure 11.3 *Characteristics for Example. 11.1*

11.1.2 Class B operation

As class B biasing puts the quiescent point close to cut-off, the transistor will only conduct on one half-cycle of an applied alternating signal. As a result, class B operation usually means arranging two transistors to operate in 'push-pull', where each transistor amplifies one half of the input signal.

The circuit shown in figure 11.4 illustrates one arrangement in which complementary NPN and PNP transistors are employed.

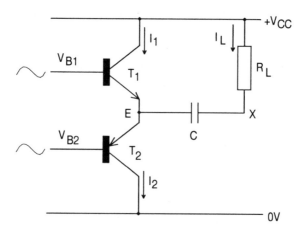

Figure 11.4 *Complementary push-pull output stage*

For true class B operation the two transistors should be biased at the cut-off point, making the quiescent current of each zero. However, this condition produces considerable amounts of 'crossover distortion' at the point where one transistor switches off and the other switches on. A much more practical biasing arrangement requires that the transistors be biased on slightly, leaving quiescent current above zero, but still very low. This is known as class AB operation.

11.1.3 Class AB operation

Consider the circuit of figure 11.4 under quiescent conditions. In order to allow the output signal to swing equal amounts about the quiescent point, biasing of the transistors is arranged so that the 'mid-point' of the output stage, point E in figure 11.4, is set to approximately half V_{cc}, e.g. 6 volts for a 12 V supply. With silicon transistors selected for T_1 and T_2, their base voltages would be about 6.7 V and 5.3 V respectively. I_1 and I_2 would be equal and close to zero and I_L would be zero, making the voltage at point X equal to V_{cc}.

The application of a signal to the bases of T_1 and T_2 would cause the following events to take place, see figure 11.5 for signal waveforms. On the negative-going half-cycle T_2 would conduct and T_1 would be turned off.

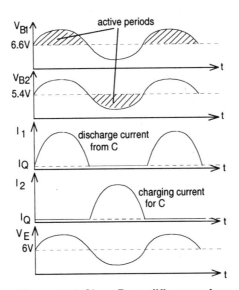

Figure 11.5 *Class B amplifier waveforms*

Current would flow from the power supply, through R_L, C and T_2 collector-emitter.

During positive-going half-cycles of input signal T_2 would turn off and T_1 would conduct. With T_2 off, there is no current path from the supply and during this period current is supplied to the load by the discharge of capacitor C. The direction of current flow in R_L is now the reverse of that for negative-going input, producing an alternating current in the load.

V_E will swing from approximately 0 V up to V_{CC}, and, as the capacitor C has a very high value (typically 1000s of μF) V_{RL} will swing by a similar amount. Hence

$$V_{RL} \text{ max} = \frac{V_{cc}}{2}$$

and

$$I_L \text{ max} = \frac{V_{cc}}{2 R_L}$$

Maximum power conversion efficiency, PCE_{max}, occurs when the voltage across R_L is at a maximum. At that point

$$\text{Maximum signal power } (P_s \text{ max}) \text{ out} = \frac{(\text{r.m.s. value of } V_{RL})^2}{R_L}$$

$$P_s \text{ max} = \frac{\left(\frac{V_{cc}}{2\sqrt{2}}\right)^2}{R_L}$$

$$\boxed{P_s \text{ max} = \frac{V_{cc}^2}{8 R_L} \text{ Watts}}$$

Power from the supply,

$$P_{DC} = V_{ave} I_{ave}$$

but

$$V_{ave} = V_{cc}$$

Average current is that taken from the supply over a full cycle, even though current is taken during one half-cycle of input signal only. The instantaneous current

$$i = I_{max} \sin \omega t$$

and the average current, I_{ave} is the integral of i for one half-cycle, i.e. from 0 to π.

$$P_{DC} = \frac{V_{DC} \int_0^\pi i}{2 \pi} \delta \omega t$$

$$P_{DC} = \frac{V_{cc}}{2 \pi} \int_0^\pi \frac{V_{cc}}{2 R_L} \sin \omega t \, \delta \omega t$$

$$P_{DC} = \frac{V_{cc}^2}{4 \pi R_L} [-\cos \pi \omega t]_0^\pi$$

$$P_{DC} = \frac{V_{cc}^2}{4 \pi R_L} [\cos 0 - \cos \pi]$$

$$P_{DC} = \frac{V_{cc}^2}{4 \pi R_L} [1 + 1]$$

$$\boxed{P_{DC} = \frac{V_{cc}^2}{2 \pi R_L} \text{ Watts}}$$

The maximum power conversion efficiency

$$PCE_{max} = \frac{\dfrac{V_{cc}^2}{8 R_L}}{\dfrac{V_{cc}^2}{2 \pi R_L}} \times 100\%$$

$$PCE_{max} = \frac{V_{cc}^2}{8 R_L} \times \frac{2 \pi R_L}{V_{cc}^2} \times 100\%$$

V_{CC2}^s and R_{LS} cancel, leaving

$$PCE_{max} = \frac{\pi}{4} \times 100\%$$

$$PCE_{max} = 78.54\%$$

11.1.4 The driver stage

Because the output transistors in the class B push-pull amplifier are operated in emitter follower configuration, the voltage gain of the circuit is slightly less than unity. A driver stage is employed to provide voltage gain and to supply the required signals to the bases of the output transistors. Figure 11.6 illustrates a typical driver stage for an output stage that employs complementary transistors.

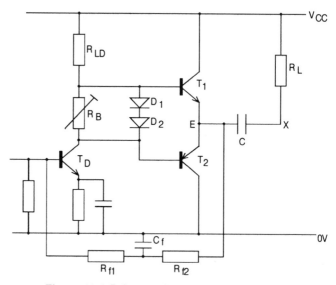

Figure 11.6 *Driver and output stages*

Referring to the circuit of figure 11.6, the diodes D_1 and D_2 are used to clamp the potential between the bases of T_1 and T_2 to twice their junction voltage ($2V_j$). As the P-N junction of a transistor experiences a rise in temperature the voltage across it, V_j, falls (by approximately 0.25 mV per °C). If a resistive biasing arrangement was employed then a fixed bias voltage would be supplied to the transistors, causing them to be biased ever further on as their operating temperature increased. This would lead to thermal runaway and the likely destruction of the transistors. The diodes, mounted on the same heat sink, and therefore, experiencing the same temperature change, maintain a potential of $2V_j$ across the transistor bases. The required voltage is set by fine adjustment of R_B.

An alternative and, generally, preferred method of stabilisation employs a transistor in the place of the diodes. Figure 11.7 illustrates the arrangement in which the transistor T_B is biased by R_{B1} and R_{B2} so that the required biasing voltage for T_1 and T_2 is developed across its collector-emitter circuit.

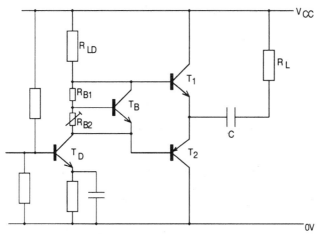

Figure 11.7 *Transistorised bias circuit*

The relationship between R_{B1}, R_{B2} and the collector-emitter potential of T_B is

$$V_{CE} = V_{BE} \left(1 + \frac{R_{B2}}{R_{B1}} \right)$$

If T_B is a silicon transistor and a bias potential of 1 volt is required, the ratio of R_{B2} to R_{B1} is approximately 0.66:1.

The voltage gain of the driver stage is determined by the value of R_{LD}. However, if a high value is selected to provide high gain, the correct biasing conditions for the output transistors are not achievable. Methods for the removal of this problem will be discussed later in this chapter.

To ensure that maximum signal power output is maintained, it is essential that point E, the 'mid-point', remains at $V_{CC}/2$. One method for achieving this is by supplying the biasing voltage for the driver transistor base from the mid-point, i.e. supplying d.c. feedback. Figure 11.8 illustrates this arrangement.

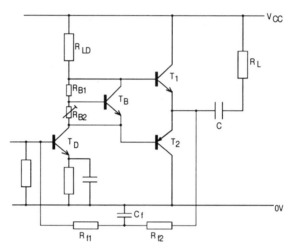

Figure 11.8 *Output stage with d.c. feedback*

Note the split resistor arrangement of R_{f1} and R_{f2} and the de-coupling capacitor C_f. The presence of C_f ensures that a.c. feedback, with its associated drop in signal gain, does not occur.

Consider a situation in which the potential at point E begins to rise due to ageing of components or changes in temperature. As the potential at point E rises, so will the base biasing voltage of T_D. This will turn T_D on more, causing its collector voltage to fall, and causing a fall in potential at point E, compensating for the original increase. Clearly, the values of R_{f1} and R_{f2} must be selected to provide the required degree of compensation.

One major problem associated with the circuit shown in figure 11.8 is that of driver stage gain - mentioned briefly earlier - being fairly low and, in certain circumstances, providing insufficient drive to operate the output transistors efficiently. Several solutions are possible, but only two will be investigated here: 'bootstrapping' and the use of compound transistors. The use of bootstrapping, the application of positive feedback from the output stage to the driver transistor collector circuit, causes an effective increase in the value of R_{LD}, without changing its actual value.

Note: The term 'bootstrapping' comes from the 'trick' that is played on the amplifier (fooling it into thinking that the driver load resistance is higher than it really is). The term comes from 'pulling oneself up by the bootstraps' - an obvious impossibility.

In one bootstrap arrangement, illustrated in figure 11.9, feedback is derived across R_L and applied to the top of R_{LD}, this resistor now being disconnected from the V_{cc} line. As previously indicated, R_{LD} must be fairly low in value to provide sufficient current drive for the output transistors.

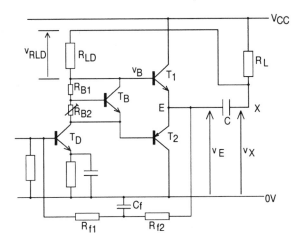

Figure 11.9 *An example of 'bootstrapping'*

Suppose that the current in T_D collector circuit causes a signal voltage across R_{LD} of 1 volt. If the voltage gain of T_1 is 0.9 then

$$V_E = V_X = 0.9 V_B$$

$$V_{RLD} = V_B - V_X$$

$$V_{RLD} = \frac{V_X}{0.9} - V_X$$

$$V_{RLD} = V_X (1.111 - 1)$$

$$V_{RLD} = 0.111 V_X$$

$$\boxed{V_X = 9 V_{RLD}}$$

This arrangement produces an effective increase in voltage gain whilst keeping R_{LD} at a low enough value to satisfy the drive requirements of the output transistors.

The second method to be described employs compound transistors, with their property of higher current gain, to provide additional current to the output transistors whilst allowing the use of a higher value resistor for R_{LD}.

The workings of compound transistors were described in chapter 5, and will not be discussed in any detail here. The circuit diagram illustrated in figure 11.10 shows two compound transistors employed as the complementary output pair. Note that the second transistor in each device is an NPN type, with signal inversion being achieved in the transistor with the PNP input arrangement.

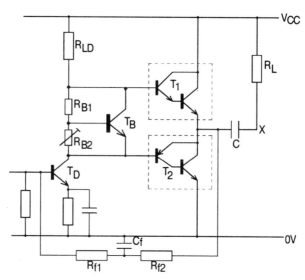

Figure 11.10 *Compound transistor output stage*

Note that with this circuit there is no longer a need for bootstrapping.

11.1.5 Short-circuit protection

Many applications of power amplifiers require the load to be remote from the amplifier, for example a public address system. In these cases the chance of a short-circuit across the load is quite high and suitable precautions must be taken when designing an amplifier to deal with such an occurrence.

Figure 11.11 shows an arrangement whereby the output transistors are protected from an over-current condition by the addition of two transistors, T_3 and T_4.

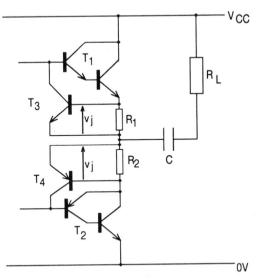

Figure 11.11 *Over-current protection circuit*

Consider a situation where a fault causes the current through R_L to increase to a level above the maximum allowable for T_1 and T_2. The values of R_1 and R_2 are selected so that such a current would produce across each resistor a voltage, V_j, sufficient to turn T_3 and T_4 on. With these transistors on, the signal applied to the bases of the output transistors T_1 and T_2 would be effectively short-circuited and the output transistors would turn off. Current in R_L would reduce to a level below an over-current situation and the transistors T_3 and T_4 would turn off, allowing T_1 and T_2 to operate again. Clearly whilst a fault is present across R_L the over-current circuit will continue to function, but as soon as the fault is cleared the amplifier should return to normal operation.

11.2 Power supplies

At earlier levels of study the unregulated (unstabilised) power supply is introduced and explained. The concepts of regulation and stabilisation are also introduced, although the two terms are often confused. In this chapter some basic power supply parameters will be considered and various designs for stabilisation and regulation will be discussed.

11.2.1 Power supply parameters

Stabilisation or line regulation

Stabilisation is the ability of a power supply to deliver a constant output voltage irrespective of changes in the input voltage. The stabilisation ratio (S) is expressed as

$$S = \frac{\delta V_o}{\delta V_{in}} \times 100\%$$

Note that the lower the value of S, the better the stabilisation.

Example 11.2

If the d.c. input to a regulator falls from 20 V to 16 V and the output voltage falls from 9.0 V to 8.9 V, calculate the stabilisation ratio.

$$S = \frac{(9.0 - 8.9) \times 100}{20 - 16} = \underline{\textbf{2.5\%}}$$

Load regulation

Load regulation is the ability of a power supply to deliver a constant voltage output irrespective of the current drawn by the load (within stated maximum output).

$$\text{Load regulation} = \frac{V_o \text{ (off load)} - V_o \text{ (full load)}}{V_o \text{ (off load)}} \times 100\%$$

The lower the output impedance of the power supply, the better the regulation will be.

Example 11.3

The output of a 12 volt regulated power supply falls to 11.5 V when the full load current of 1 amp is drawn. Calculate the load regulation of the supply.

$$Load\ regulation = \frac{12 - 11.5}{12} \times 100\%$$

Load regulation = 4.16%

Output impedance

When current is being drawn from a power supply, its output voltage will always be lower than the voltage source due to the series source resistance, r_o, illustrated in figure 11.12.

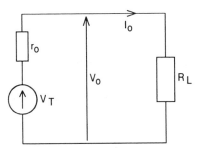

Figure 11.12 *Thévenin equivalent circuit of PSU*

Example 11.4

Taking the data from example 11.3
$V_T = 12\ V$, $V_o = 11.5\ V$ and $I_o = 1\ A$.

$$r_o = \frac{12 - 11.5}{1} = \underline{0.5\Omega}$$

Thermal regulation

This is a measure of the percentage change in output from its nominal value due to changes in operating temperature.

Transient response

This parameter describes the time that it takes for the output of the power supply to react to a sudden change in line or load conditions, and is often referred to as the 'recovery time'.

Efficiency

The power output of a power supply will always be less than the power input to it, some power being dissipated as heat in the internal components of the power supply. The efficiency of a power supply is the available power output as a percentage of power in, i.e.

$$\eta = \frac{P_{out}}{P_{in}} \times 100\%$$

11.2.2 Regulated power supplies

All regulated power supplies employ a reference voltage and compare the output of the supply with the reference level in order to determine what, if any, changes need to be made. In this book two popular types of regulator circuit will be considered, the linear regulator and the switched-mode power supply (SMPS).

The reference voltage is usually derived from a zener or reverse-breakdown diode. Two effects cause a reverse-voltage breakdown, avalanche breakdown and zener breakdown. It is not the author's intention to delve into the details of each type of breakdown other than to indicate the practical issues arising from them. Zener breakdown occurs when the cathode voltage of the diode exceeds its anode voltage by between 2.5 and 5 volts. Avalanche breakdown occurs at cathode-anode voltages in excess of 7 volts. The practical issues revolve around the temperature coefficients of these two effects. Avalanche breakdown voltage increases as junction temperature increases but zener breakdown voltage decreases with an increase in junction temperature. There is, as a result, a range of breakdown voltages, i.e. between 5 and 7 volts, in which a change in temperature causes equal and opposite changes in avalanche and zener breakdown voltages. Reverse-voltage breakdown diodes that operate in this voltage range have approximately zero temperature coefficients and are employed as voltage reference diodes.

The series regulator

The basic series regulator is a linear circuit that takes d.c. from an unregulated power supply and exerts line and load regulation. A transistor is connected in series with the d.c. output and the availability of output current, i.e. that current supplied by the transistor, is determined by the biasing potential on its base. The bias for the transistor is maintained at a stable value by a reference voltage source, often a zener diode. The transistor provides current gain such that a large change in output current can be compensated for with a small change in base current and, therefore, a small change in zener diode current. If, for example, the transistor has a current gain of 50 then a change in output current of 1 amp can be corrected with a suitable change of base current of 20 mA. Figure 11.13 shows the circuit arrangement for the series regulator.

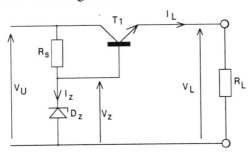

Figure 11.13 *A simple series regulator*

The zener diode D_z acts as both reference and stabiliser. Under no-load conditions I_z is flowing in the diode, providing the voltage V_z to bias the transistor. As the transistor is connected as an emitter-follower the output voltage, V_o will be equal to the zener voltage less the base-emitter voltage of T_1, i.e.

$$V_L = V_Z - V_{BE}$$

Under these conditions the maximum bias current is flowing in the diode with virtually no current in the base of the transistor. For example, if the maximum current that can be delivered by the power supply is 1 A, then, with a current gain of 50, I_z will equal 20 mA. When the maximum load current is being drawn, i.e. $I_0 = 1$ A, the current in the base of the transistor will be 20 mA and the current in the zener diode will be at its minimum (but not zero, as some current must flow in the zener diode to maintain regulation). If the change in current in the zener diode is kept small then the regulation provided by the diode is improved - hence the use of the transistor.

Suppose that the load current increases within the specifications of the power supply. As the base potential is held constant by the reference voltage the fall in emitter voltage will produce an increase in base-emitter potential. This causes the transistor to conduct more and supply the extra current required by the load.

The main disadvantage of this simple circuit is that, due to its internal resistance, any changes in current in the zener diode produce a change in its zener voltage. This produces a degree of regulation that is insufficient for many applications.

A development of the simple series regulator involves feeding back a proportion of the output voltage and comparing it with a stable reference voltage. As changes in output voltage occur a correcting signal is applied to the series regulator to compensate for the original change. The block diagram for a 'comparator regulator' comprises a voltage reference, a feedback network, a comparator and a series regulator as illustrated in figure 11.14.

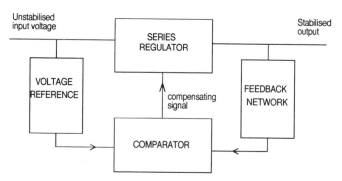

Figure 11.14 *Comparator regulator block diagram*

The comparator stage often provides a degree of amplification from a transistor or op-amp. This feature allows current changes in the comparator stage to be kept very small, improving the overall regulation offered by the circuit. A practical circuit, employing a transistor comparator is shown in figure 11.15.

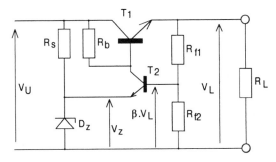

Figure 11.15 *A basic comparator regulator circuit*

In figure 11.15 the feedback network of R_{f1} and R_{f2} is connected across V_L feeding a proportion of the output voltage back to the base of the comparator/amplifier, T_2. With the emitter of T_2 held constant by D_z, any changes in βV_L will cause a larger change at the base of T_1, providing compensation by altering the base-emitter biasing of T_1. The feedback fraction, β, is set by the potential divider network of R_{f1} and R_{f2}, such that

$$\beta = \frac{R_{f2}}{R_{f1} + R_{f2}}$$

The use of an operational amplifier in a comparator regulator circuit improves stability due to the very high open-loop gain of the op-amp. Figure 11.16 illustrates the circuit arrangement for an op-amp comparator/amplifier.

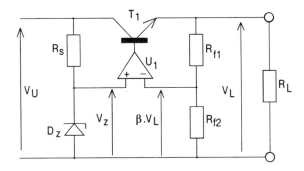

Figure 11.16 *Op-amp comparator/amplifier*

If the output voltage falls, so the feedback voltage, βV_L , applied to the inverting terminal of the op-amp, follows. This causes the output of the op-amp to rise, increasing the base-emitter potential of T_1 and producing a rise in output voltage.

Improvements in performance can be effected as follows

    ❑   replace the series regulator transistor with a compound (Darlington) transistor

    ❑   fit a smoothing capacitor across the zener diode to remove the small amounts of ripple present

    ❑   employ two zener diodes as a reference voltage source. This has the advantage of reducing the current in the reference diode and thereby improving its zener voltage stability.

11.2.3 Integrated circuit regulators

There is a range of i.c. power supply regulators available to the electronics designer. Most of these devices are for low voltage use, typically ±5 or ±12 volt output, although variable output may be obtained with the addition of a few components.

In its basic form the i.c. regulator circuit employs about four components, the i.c. and three others.

Figure 11.17 illustrates an arrangement which includes protection diodes and a variable output voltage.

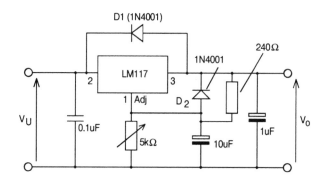

Figure 11.17 *Circuit from SGS Semiconductor Ltd*

In the circuit shown in figure 11.17 D_1 protects the regulator i.c. from a short-circuit on the input whilst D_2 protects against output short-circuit during capacitor discharge.

11.2.4 Protection circuits

A power supply must be protected from two major fault conditions, over-current, where a faulty external circuit draws excessive current from the supply, and over-voltage, where the supply exhibits an internal fault and supplies too much voltage at its output(s).

Over-current protection

A power supply must be prevented from supplying, or attempting to supply, a current in excess of its rated output. To this end a circuit that senses the level of output current must be incorporated into the output circuitry of the supply. Having detected an over-current situation, the sensing circuit must alter the performance of the supply, reducing the ability of the supply to deliver current, until the fault condition has been removed.

The circuit shown in figure 11.18 is of an over-current detection circuit in which a low-value resistor, R_{oc}, is placed in series with the output of the supply.

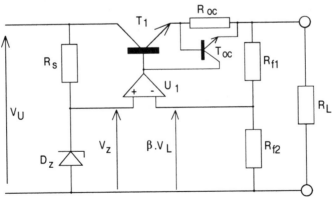

Figure 11.18 *Over-current protection circuit*

The value of the resistor is selected in order that any level of current through it that exceeds the maximum level prescribed for the supply will generate sufficient voltage across the resistor to switch transistor T_{oc} **on**. The collector-emitter voltage of T_{oc} will fall, shunting the base-emitter circuit of the series regulator transistor, restricting the current delivered by the supply.

Example 11.5

For a maximum current of 5 A, and a silicon transistor as T_{oc}, calculate the required value of R_{oc} to provide adequate over-current protection.

$$R = \frac{V}{I} = \frac{0.65}{5} = \underline{\mathbf{0.13\,\Omega}}$$

There are many other methods for preventing damage from an over-current condition but these will not be discussed here.

Over-voltage protection

The major consideration when a power supply generates an internal fault is the damage that can be caused to external circuits. It is essential, therefore, that any over-voltage condition be detected and corrected as quickly as possible. One circuit that is often employed for this purpose uses a Silicon Controlled Rectifier (SCR) connected across the power supply output (this arrangement is often called a 'crowbar'). Figure 11.19 illustrates an arrangement in which a crowbar is placed after an over-current sensing circuit.

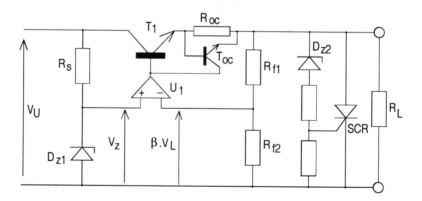

Figure 11.19 *Over-voltage protection circuit*

If an over-voltage condition arises, the voltage across the zener diode D_{z2} exceeds the breakdown level and the zener conducts. The SCR is switched **on** and a low resistance is effectively connected across the supply output rails. An over-current condition is generated and the over-current protection circuit is activated causing the series regulator to shut down.

11.2.5 The shunt stabiliser

Although the series regulator circuit is very popular it does have the disadvantage that the series regulator transistor has to carry the full load current of the power supply. For very high current supply a shunt stabiliser is often preferred. In this arrangement a transistor is connected across the power supply rails and, therefore, must bear a relatively high voltage at all times but will only bear the full load current when the output is open-circuit.

The principle of operation of the shunt stabiliser is that the transistor will draw an amount of current to compensate for changes in load current, providing the unregulated supply with a constant current demand. As load current falls so current in the shunt transistor must increase to compensate for this. Figure 11.20 shows a very simple arrangement that employs many of the circuits already described for the series regulator circuit.

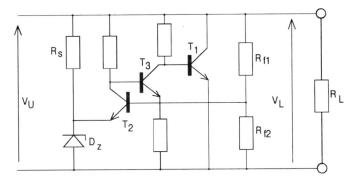

Figure 11.20 *A simple shunt regulator*

Suppose that the load current increases causing a drop in output potential. The voltage on the base of T_2 will fall making T_2 collector rise. This will turn T_3 on more, causing the base of the shunt stabiliser T_1 to fall and making T_1 conduct less. With suitable biasing of T_1, T_2 and T_3 any change in load current should be compensated for in T_1.

11.2.6 The switched-mode power supply

Switched mode power supplies (SMPS) are essentially d.c. to d.c. converters operating at ultrasonic frequencies, typically in the range 20 kHz to 100
kHz. The SMPS stores energy during one part of the conversion cycle and
distributes that energy during the remaining time. The main advantages of
the switched mode power supply are

- □ higher efficiency than linear regulators, typically 70-90% compared with 30-50%
- □ less power dissipation, allowing them to run cooler
- □ smaller size due to lower values for capacitors and inductors
  operating at higher frequencies

One significant disadvantage is the lower level of ripple rejection obtained.
There is also a problem of increased electromagnetic and radio frequency
interference (emi and rfi) generated by the SMPS.

Although there are several types of switched mode power supply this book
will discuss only one type - the flyback converter.

The basic arrangement of the SMPS is similar to that of the comparator
regulator described earlier. However, the output of the switched mode
power supply is controlled by adjusting the duty cycle of a high frequency
transistor switch. Figure 11.21 illustrates the arrangement of circuits for a
basic SMPS.

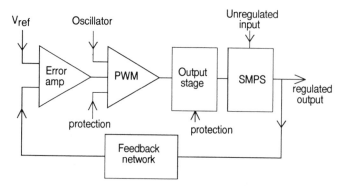

Figure 11.21 *Block diagram of a SMPS*

Figure 11.21 is reproduced courtesy of **Linear LSI Products**.

The SMPS block consists of a transistor and a transformer. The transistor is switching at a high frequency and the output waveform is smoothed to provide a d.c. output. A fraction of the output is fed back, via the feedback network, to an error amplifier and compared with a reference voltage. The output of the error amplifier controls the width of an oscillator pulse in the PWM (Pulse Width Modulator) block. As the width of the pulse is varied, so is the duty cycle of the SMPS transistor, in turn controlling the output of the power supply.

Note the protection inputs to the PWM and Output stage blocks.

Many SMPS integrated circuits are currently available, including

- □ μA78S40PN   Motorola

- □ L296   SGS Thomson

- □ MAX 743   Maxim

- □ NE5561   Philips Semiconductors

12 Software Simulation

The high cost of researching, designing and testing electronic circuits and their subsequent modification and retesting has led many electronic equipment manufacturers to employ computer programs to simulate the action of an electronic circuit design prior to its construction.

Both analogue and digital circuits can be simulated but, in general, programs that can do both types of circuit are rare. This book will deal only with analogue or 'linear' circuit analysis.

The subject of software simulation and analysis is too vast and detailed to be covered in a single chapter and, therefore, the extent to which the subject will be covered here is limited to basic program operations, including

- □ loading an existing circuit into the simulation software
- □ performing an analysis on an existing circuit
- □ modifying a circuit

Two software packages will be employed for these purposes, 'TopSpice' and 'Analyser III' (see end of this chapter for details on where to obtain these programs). The text will include response curves 'captured' from a computer screen to illustrate the responses of a number of circuits described earlier in this book. The two programs that will be used for this chapter both employ component 'models' connected in a network, with connections (circuit junctions) referred to as *nodes* (TopSpice) or *signals* (Analyser).

Note that Analyser calls a point on the response curve a 'node' whereas TopSpice (a Spice derivative) calls a circuit junction a 'node'.

Both programs provide a library of predetermined component models for use by a designer, but also allow the design of new models which can be added to the library for future use. Each component is identified by a name, for example 'R' for a resistor, 'C' for a capacitor, etc., and each component must have a set of parameters. Clearly, active components such as transistors and op-amps will have more parameters than passive components like resistors, capacitors and inductors (more details will be given when the programs are described later). The information regarding the types of components and the interconnections that form the circuit is contained in a netlist *or* netfile, *an* ASCII text file that may be produced by a text editor or word processor. Netlists may also be produced by schematic design and capture programs which allow the designer to create schematic diagrams with computer software.

Such schematic capture programs are available for both TopSpice and Analyser III and will be identified later in this chapter.

Having produced the netlist, the designer can go on to produce a circuit response, over a selected range of frequencies, indicating circuit gain, phase, input or output impedance, group delay or noise response. The advantages of circuit analysis by computer simulation are as follows

- □ component values may be changed and the circuit reanalysed in order to identify the effects of the change
- □ practical components may be replaced with 'ideal' components in order to detect the source of circuit losses
- □ minor or major circuit changes can be made and their effect observed and recorded.
- □ different designs can be compared to find the most efficient circuit

There are some words of caution regarding the use of software simulation and analysis of circuits.

- □ It is important to realise that analysis is performed according to a prescribed 'model' of a component. The designer should be aware of the model being used and the assumptions that are made in that model.
- □ It may be cheaper, in both time and money, to build and test a simple circuit than to use software to analyse its performance.

    □   Before any production run is initiated the circuit should be built and thoroughly tested in order to confirm the analysis produced by the circuit simulation software.

12.1 TopSpice

TopSpice is a derivative of SPICE, an electronic circuit analysis program developed at the University of California at Berkeley during the early 1970s. SPICE is an acronym for Simulation Program with Integrated Circuit Emphasis and the program has become the standard for linear circuit analysis. Various programs have taken the SPICE standard and developed it further, some incorporating schematic capture, some including digital circuit simulation, some doing both of these. All of these programs employ the numeric algorithms and circuit conventions of the generic SPICE program. TopSpice can accept netlists produced by its family program 'TopNet', a graphical 'front-end' and schematic capture program and then display and modify the response of a circuit with another program 'TopView', described as a 'graphics post-processor'. The author has used a demonstration version of the program to produce the circuits and plots shown in this chapter. See the end of this chapter for details of how to obtain a free evaluation copy of the software.

TopSpice, like SPICE, has three modes of operation, allowing DC, AC and transient analysis. This book will be limited to the AC analysis of circuits, in line with the general discussions of circuit parameters and performance.

12.1.1 Starting TopSpice

Having installed TopSpice on to the hard disk of an IBM®-compatible personal computer and changing to the appropriate directory, the program is executed by typing 'ts' at the DOS prompt. The program user is then greeted with an initial list of options, these being

    NEW Circuit File
    CAPTURE/Edit Schematic
    EDIT/Create Circuit File
    ANALYSIS Options
    Run **SIMULATION**

PLOT Results (run post-processor)
BROWSE Output File
DOS Command
QUIT

From this opening menu select **NEW Circuit File** and press <ENTER> to see a list of available circuit files (those with a .CIR file extension). Using the cursor keys to highlight the required file name, press <ENTER> to select and load the circuit called OPAMP.CIR. This is an analysis of an operational amplifier in which DC, AC and transient characteristics are produced, although the user is allowed to select any or all of the three for plotting. Having loaded a circuit file it is possible to view the schematic diagram by selecting **CAPTURE/Edit Schematic** at the main menu. The circuit for OPAMP.CIR is illustrated in figure 12.1.

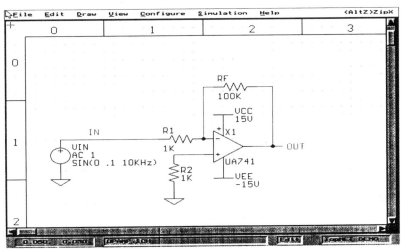

Figure 12.1 *The TopSpice schematic design screen*

Note that the AC signal source has an amplitude of 1 volt (the line commencing SIN ... relates to the transient analysis that is performed in this example and will not be considered here).

Examination of the options available indicates that various additions and/or modifications may be carried out on the circuit prior to any analysis taking place. For example, components may be added, existing components may be moved, copied or deleted, the parameters (e.g. values, names) can be changed and SPICE commands may be added to the circuit file. Circuit nodes may be displayed if required, allowing easier reference to the circuit file. When you are happy with the circuit select **Exit** from the **File** menu of the schematic design program to return to the main menu. The circuit may be analysed by selecting **Run SIMULATION** or, prior to that, the circuit file may be examined by selecting **EDIT/Create Circuit File** from the main menu. The text file for OPAMP.CIR is reproduced in the window below.

As the DC and transient analyses are not required they can be removed from the example by deleting the lines in the circuit file shown in italics.

OPAMP (UA741) TEST CIRCUIT

VCC vcc 0 15V
VEE vee 0 -15V
VIN in 0 SIN (0 0.1 10KHz) AC 1

RS1 in 2 1K
RS2 1 0 1K
RF out 2 100K
XG 1 2 vcc vee out UA741

.DC VIN -0.25 0.25 0.005
.PRINT DC V(out)

.AC DEC 10 1 10GHz
.PRINT AC VDB(out) VP(out)

.TRAN 5u 250us
.PRINT TRAN/ALL V(in) V(out)

.END

The title of the analysis file appears on the first line of the circuit listing **and may not be placed elsewhere.**

The line *.AC DEC 10 1 10GHz* means perform an AC analysis over 10 decades, from f = 1 Hz to f=10 GHz.

The line *.PRINT AC VDB(out) VP(out)* allows a plot of the gain, in dBs, and phase at the circuit node labelled **out** (**OUT**).

The other lines describe the various circuit components and their connections within the circuit.

Note the use of numbers and names for the circuit nodes, e.g. IN, OUT, VCC and VEE.

Selecting Run **SIMULATION** from the main menu will cause full circuit analysis to take place and the screen messages keep the user informed at all stages of the process (although these may be difficult to read on fast machines). Having completed the analysis without generating an error message (errors are reported quite satisfactorily - with quite clear indications of the nature and position of the error) the **PROBE** program must be executed by clicking the mouse button on the Probe option bar. This is a graphics post-processor which performs the actions of a 'software oscilloscope', displaying a variety of waveforms including magnitude (ratio), logarithmic magnitude, phase, transient response, etc. This example circuit analysis offers **IN**, **VDB(out)** (effectively the gain of the amplifier as vin is 1 volt) and **VP(out)** (phase of vout) as possible nodes (see earlier circuit listing description). However, the default condition, selected if no parameters are attached to the .**PROBE** line in the circuit file, offers a plot of signals at every point in the circuit. Selecting **VDB(out)** and pressing the F10 key (to indicate completion) will cause the plot menu to be shown. Selecting **Magnitude** or **Logarithmic Magnitude (dB)** will produce a graphical representation of the gain response of the amplifier, as indicated in figure 12.2. A further range of options are offered in this phase of the analysis, including adding and removing traces, placing cursors at points of interest on the response curve and more.

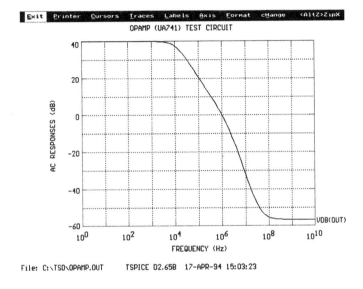

Figure 12.2 *Screen captured from TopSpice*

The evaluation version of TopSpice will not allow a printout to be obtained, although the facility is present in the full version. However, with suitable screen capture software, an on-screen image can be saved to disc and reproduced in word processing and desktop publishing software, albeit with considerable degradation of image quality.

A further example is as follows. A second order, high pass active filter (see the circuit listing below and the circuit in figure 12.3) is analysed and produces the response as illustrated in figure 12.4.

```
2nd ORDER HPF

VIN 1 0 SIN (0 0.1 10KHz) AC 1
VCC VCC 0 +12V
VEE VEE 0 -12V

X1 3 4 VCC VEE OUT UA741
R1 4 OUT 22.5k
R2 2 OUT 11.25k
R3 3 0 22.5k
C1 2 3 10nF
C2 1 2 10nF

.AC DEC 10 1 10MEG

.PRINT AC VDB(OUT) VP(OUT)

.END
```

Note the use of MEG not MHz.

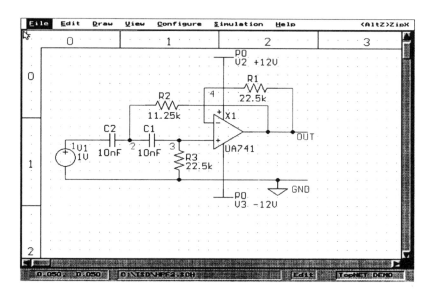

Figure 12.3 *High pass filter in TopSpice*

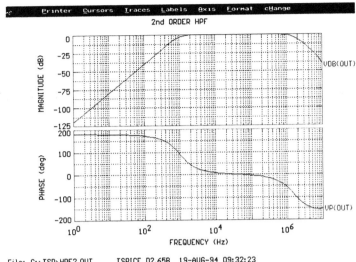

Figure 12.4 *High pass filter response curve*

12.2 Analyser III

Analyser III is a linear analogue circuit analysis program that runs on IBM (International Business Machines Inc.)-compatible personal computers and can perform AC analysis of circuits. Netlists can be created within the program or by use of a separate text editor. The company that produces Analyser also produces a schematic 'front end' called EASY PC Professional for use with Analyser.

In the first exercise, an example circuit will be loaded into Analyser and an analysis performed.

Note that Analyser uses the .NET file extension for its circuits.

From the **File** menu select **Load a circuit.**

You are offered ***.NET** (that is all circuit files present in the selected disc directory). Press the ENTER key to see all of the file names.

Select **AMP.NET**

By default Analyser will produce a gain/phase response with 20 points plotted. The plot for AMP.NET, captured from the computer screen, is reproduced in figure 12.5.

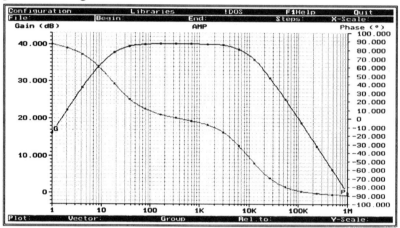

Figure 12.5 *Plot of Analyser example 'AMP.NET'*

Note that the colour screen of Analyser III has been converted to grey scales for this book. The gain response is identified with a 'G' at the left-hand Y axis, and the phase response with a 'P' on the right-hand Y axis. It can be seen from the response that the amplifier has a gain of approximately 40 dB in mid band, and that roll-off takes place at both low and high frequency ends of the response. Examination of the netlist file with a text editor would reveal the following

/R1[R]	/R3[R]	/A1[A]
[A=1]	[A=3]	[IN+=1]
[B=4]	[B=2]	[IN-=2]
R:100000	R:10000	[OUT=3]
#	#	#
/R2[R]	/C1[C]	
[A=2]	[A=0]	
[B=4]	[B=1]	
R:100	C:.0000001	
#	#	

The '/' character denotes a new component contained in a block of four lines and terminated with the '#' symbol, for example '/R1[R]' indicates a resistor

[R] with the name R1, connected between points 1 and 4 in the circuit and having a value of 100,000 Ω.

Note that the capacitor's value is shown in farads, i. e. C1 is 0.1 µF.

Unlike SPICE, Analyser III does not reserve a particular connection label for the signal ground, connection 4 in this circuit. Of course, reference to the netlist will allow the drawing of the circuit diagram, in this case a non-inverting amplifier employing an op-amp and illustrated in figure 12.6.

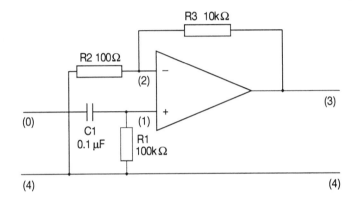

Figure 12.6 *C-R coupled non-inverting amplifier*

Having created a circuit (saved with a **.NET** file extension) an analysis can be performed by the user specifying the frequency range of interest and whether a gain/phase, input/output impedance or group delay response is required.

Further information

Analyser III is obtainable from

Number One Systems Ltd
Harding Way
Somersham Road
St. Ives
Huntingdon
Cambridgeshire, England. PE17 4WR

The TopSpice family of programs is available in the U.K. from

CRaG Systems
8 Shakespeare Road
Thatcham
Newbury
Berks.
RG13 4DG

Tel. 0635 873670

an evaluation version available at no charge (at the time of writing, i.e. September 1994).

A: Laboratory Experiments

The following suggestions for laboratory experiments are to reinforce certain aspects of some of the circuits explained in the earlier chapters of this book. They have been placed at the end of the book, rather than within a chapter, as some of them incorporate circuits from a number of chapters. In this respect, some of the experiments may be considered as Integrated Assignments, bringing together a variety of analogue (and digital) electronics circuits.

1. Determination of f_2 of an amplifier

Employing a variety of techniques, determine the upper cut-off frequency, f_2, of the first stage of a C-R coupled cascaded small-signal amplifier. Three possible techniques are

- ☐ measuring the voltage gain over a range of frequencies (clearly around f_2), plotting a graph of Gain (in dB) against log f and reading the value of f_2 from the graph
- ☐ calculating f_2 from the expression $f_2 = \dfrac{1}{2\,\pi\,C_s\,R_p}$, taking care to measure accurately the values of the relevant components
- ☐ applying a rectangular waveform at the input of the amplifier, measuring the rise time of the output signal and calculating f_2 from the expression $f_2 = \dfrac{0.35}{t_r}$

The three methods will probably produce different values for f_2. Your analysis of the experiment results should include an investigation into the possible sources of error present in each of the methods employed. Careful evaluation of the error sources should enable the reader to determine which, if any, of the values of f_2 is closest to the actual cut-off frequency.

2. Frequency-sensitive TTL switching circuit

In this experiment the reader employs two circuits discussed earlier in this book, plus a precision op-amp based half-wave rectifier and a d.c. level changer often employed in digital electronics to change signal voltage levels to TTL or CMOS requirements.

A signal generator is employed to generate a sine wave of a prescribed frequency, for example 1 kHz. A tuned collector amplifier is employed to produce an amplified output at around the desired frequency. The precision rectifier and associated smoothing circuit are then used to produce a d.c. signal proportional to the amplitude of the amplifier output. The d.c. signal is then applied to a voltage comparator in order to generate a rapidly switching output sufficient to control a logic circuit. Finally the switching voltage must be converted to 0 and +5 V, suitable for a TTL gate. Of course, having generated the TTL-compatible switching signal it may be used to control any TTL circuit.

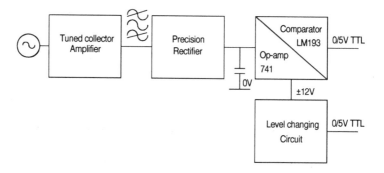

Figure A.1 *Block diagram of overall system*

Note that the use of a dedicated comparator such as the LM193 will provide a TTL-compatible output without the need for the level changing circuit.

When designing the tuned-collector amplifier, the experimenter should select one of the tuned-circuit components, usually the inductor, and calculate the value of the other to obtain the required frequency of operation.

The reader will recognise most of the blocks in figure A.1, with the exception of the precision rectifier, details of which will follow. Such rectifying circuits may be half-wave or full-wave operation and I have selected a half-wave circuit for this application, see figure A.2.

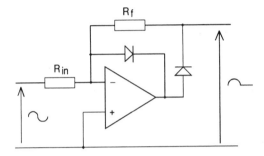

Figure A.2 *Half-wave precision rectifier*

As with a conventional inverting amplifier, the gain of this circuit is determined, by the ratio R_f / R_{in}.

The value of the smoothing capacitor (shown in the block diagram) depends upon the frequency of the signal that is to be detected, as little current will be drawn by the comparator following it. At 1 kHz a value between 0.1 and 1.0 μF is quite sufficient to provide an adequate d.c. signal.

In order to determine values for the comparator resistances the d.c. output from the precision rectifier/smoothing circuit must be known. A suitable reference voltage may then be selected and a decision taken as to whether hysteresis is needed for the comparator.

3. Rectangular/triangular waveform generator

Tasks

(a) Build, test and record/sketch the transfer characteristic for

☐ a zero-crossing detector without hysteresis
☐ a reference level detector without hysteresis
☐ a zero-crossing detector with hysteresis

(b) Build and test an op-amp based integrator

Apply a d.c. potential from a power supply to the input of the integrator and observe the output of the circuit on an oscilloscope. Note the relationship between the fixed input voltage and the changing output signal.

Note: It may be necessary (by employing large values for C and R) to make the rate of change of output very low (in the order of seconds) in order to monitor the output.

(c) Construct, test and measure/record the frequency of operation of a waveform generator as described in chapter 8 of this book.

Calculate the frequency of operation and compare the calculated and measured results. Conduct an investigation into the cause of any discrepancies between the two results.

4. A-D and D-A converters

(a) Analogue to digital converter

In this experiment you will construct a very simple 'flash' converter, employing several voltage comparators, see figure A.3. The outputs of the comparators produce what is known as a 'thermometer' code which is then decoded by an appropriate logic circuit to produce the normal 8-4-2-1 binary code expected from a D-A converter. In practice these very fast converters would have anything from 256 comparators upwards (256 comparators are required for an 8-bit binary output).

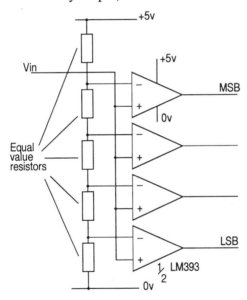

Figure A.3 *Flash converter with 5 output levels*

Single comparators, such as the LM193, may be employed in the circuit or, alternatively, several multiple-device packages are available, for example, the LM393 dual comparator. With a 5 volt supply and 5 equal value resistors, for example 1 kΩ each, there will be a 1 volt difference between the reference voltages for the comparators. Hence, the relationship between the analogue input voltage and the thermometer output code will be as illustrated in the following table.

Analogue input	Digital output code
0 - 1 volts	0000
1 - 2 volts	0001
2 - 3 volts	0011
3 - 4 volts	0111
4 - 5 volts	1111

(b) Digital to analogue converter

Build and test an 8-4-2-1 D-A converter that employs a summing amplifier and four 8-4-2-1 weighted resistors, as described in chapter 6 and illustrated in figure A.4.

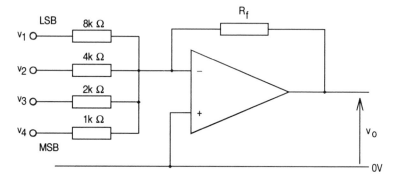

Figure A.4 *Suggested values for 8-4-2-1 DAC*

Note that the feedback resistor may be any value depending upon how much gain is required from the converter.

B: Data Sheets

The following few pages show extracts from manufacturers' data books for several example devices. These devices have been selected to demonstrate the advances made in device specification due to the development, by companies like Texas Instruments, Philips Semiconductors and Maxim Integrated Products, of new and varied semiconductor materials and technologies. For example, an operational amplifier, the TLE2027, with an open-loop gain of 153 dB (or, as a ratio, approximately 44.6 million!) from Texas Instruments, an op-amp, the 5539, with a slew rate of 600 V/μs from Philips Semiconductors and a switch mode power supply controller, the LT1074, from Maxim Integrated Products.

In addition, data on the ageing 741, available from most mainstream integrated circuit manufacturers but, in this instance, from Texas Instruments and a comparator, LM193, from Philips Semiconductors are included.

The following pages are reproduced by kind permission of

- ☐ Texas Instruments Ltd.
- ☐ Philips Semiconductors Ltd. Please note that

- ☐ Maxim Integrated Products (UK) Ltd.

uA741C, uA741I, uA741M
GENERAL-PURPOSE OPERATIONAL AMPLIFIERS

D920, NOVEMBER 1970 — REVISED JANUARY 1992

- Short-Circuit Protection

- Offset-Voltage Null Capability

- Large Common-Mode and Differential Voltage Ranges

- No Frequency Compensation Required

- Low Power Consumption

- No Latch-Up

- Designed to Be Interchangeable With Fairchild μA741

description

The uA741 is a general-purpose operational amplifier featuring offset-voltage null capability.

The high common-mode input voltage range and the absence of latch-up make the amplifier ideal for voltage-follower applications. The device is short-circuit protected and the internal frequency compensation ensures stability without external components. A low potentiometer may be connected between the offset null inputs to null out the offset voltage as shown in Figure 2.

The uA741C is characterized for operation from 0°C to 70°C. The uA741I is characterized for operation from −40°C to 85°C. The uA741M is characterized for operation over the full military temperature range of −55°C to 125°C.

symbol

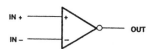

uA741M . . . J PACKAGE
(TOP VIEW)

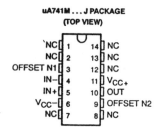

uA741M . . . JG PACKAGE
uA741C, uA741I . . . D OR P PACKAGE
(TOP VIEW)

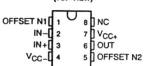

uA741M . . . U FLAT PACKAGE
(TOP VIEW)

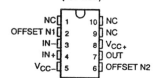

uA741M . . . FK PACKAGE
(TOP VIEW)

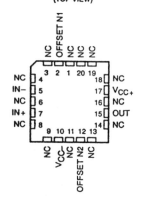

NC–No internal connection

uA741C, uA741I, uA741M
GENERAL-PURPOSE OPERATIONAL AMPLIFIERS

AVAILABLE OPTIONS

T_A	PACKAGE					
	SMALL OUTLINE (D)	CHIP CARRIER (FK)	CERAMIC DIP (J)	CERAMIC DIP (JG)	PLASTIC DIP (P)	FLAT PACK (U)
0°C to 70°C	uA741CD				uA741CP	
−40°C to 85°C	uA741ID				uA741IP	
−55°C to 125°C		uA741MFK	uA741MJ	uA741MJG		uA741MU

The D package is available taped and reeled. Add the suffix R (e.g., uA741CDR).

schematic

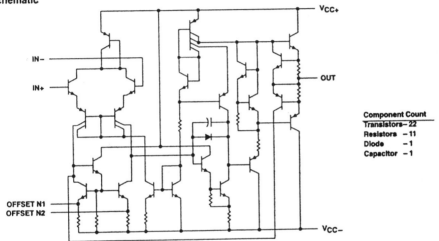

Component Count
Transistors – 22
Resistors – 11
Diode – 1
Capacitor – 1

absolute maximum ratings over operating free-air temperature range (unless otherwise noted)

		uA741C	uA741I	uA741M	UNIT
Supply voltage V_{CC+} (see Note 1)		18	22	22	V
Supply voltage V_{CC-} (see Note 1)		−18	−22	−22	V
Differential input voltage (see Note 2)		±15	±30	±30	V
Input voltage any input (see Notes 1 and 3)		±15	±15	±15	V
Voltage between either offset null terminal (N1/N2) and V_{CC-}		±15	±0.5	±0.5	V
Duration of output short circuit (see Note 4)		unlimited	unlimited	unlimited	
Continuous total power dissipation		See Dissipation Rating Table			
Operating free-air temperature range		0 to 70	−40 to 85	−55 to 125	°C
Storage temperature range		−65 to 150	−65 to 150	−65 to 150	°C
Case temperature for 60 seconds	FK package			260	°C
Lead temperature 1,6 mm (1/16 inch) from case for 60 seconds	J, JG, or U package			300	°C
Lead temperature 1,6 mm (1/16 inch) from case for 10 seconds	D or P package	260	260		°C

NOTES: 1. All voltage values, unless otherwise noted, are with respect to the midpoint between V_{CC+} and V_{CC-}.
2. Differential voltages are at the noninverting input terminal with respect to the inverting input terminal.
3. The magnitude of the input voltage must never exceed the magnitude of the supply voltage or 15 V, whichever is less.
4. The output may be shorted to ground or either power supply. For the uA741M only, the unlimited duration of the short circuit applies at (or below) 125°C case temperature or 75°C free-air temperature.

uA741C, uA741I, uA741M
GENERAL-PURPOSE OPERATIONAL AMPLIFIERS

DISSIPATION RATING TABLE

PACKAGE	$T_A \leq 25°C$ POWER RATING	DERATING FACTOR	DERATE ABOVE T_A	$T_A = 70°C$ POWER RATING	$T_A = 85°C$ POWER RATING	$T_A = 125°C$ POWER RATING
D	500 mW	5.8 mW/°C	64°C	464 mW	377 mW	N/A
FK	500 mW	11.0 mW/°C	105°C	500 mW	500 mW	275 mW
J	500 mW	11.0 mW/°C	105°C	500 mW	500 mW	275 mW
JG	500 mW	8.4 mW/°C	90°C	500 mW	500 mW	210 mW
P	500 mW	N/A	N/A	500 mW	500 mW	N/A
U	500 mW	5.4 mW/°C	57°C	432 mW	351 mW	135 mW

electrical characteristics at specified free-air temperature, $V_{CC\pm} = \pm15$ V

PARAMETER		TEST CONDITIONS	T_A[†]	UA741C MIN	TYP	MAX	UA741I, UA741M MIN	TYP	MAX	UNIT
V_{IO}	Input offset voltage	$V_O = 0$	25°C		1	6		1	5	mV
			Full range			7.5			6	
$\Delta V_{IO(adj)}$	Offset voltage adjust range	$V_O = 0$	25°C		±15			±15		mV
I_{IO}	Input offset current	$V_O = 0$	25°C		20	200		20	200	nA
			Full range			300			500	
I_{IB}	Input bias current	$V_O = 0$	25°C		80	500		80	500	nA
			Full range			800			1500	
V_{ICR}	Common-mode input voltage range		25°C	±12	±13		±12	±13		V
			Full range	±12			±12			
V_{OM}	Maximum peak output voltage swing	$R_L = 10$ kΩ	25°C	±12	±14		±12	±14		V
		$R_L \geq 10$ kΩ	Full range	±12			±12			
		$R_L = 2$ kΩ	25°C	±10	±13		±10	±13		
		$R_L \geq 2$ kΩ	Full range	±10			±10			
A_{VD}	Large-signal differential voltage amplification	$R_L \geq 2$ kΩ $V_O = \pm10$ V	25°C	20	200		50	200		V/mV
			Full range	15			25			
r_i	Input resistance		25°C	0.3	2		0.3	2		MΩ
r_o	Output resistance	$V_O = 0$, See Note 5	25°C		75			75		Ω
C_i	Input capacitance		25°C		1.4			1.4		pF
CMRR	Common-mode rejection ratio	$V_{IC} = V_{ICR}$ min	25°C	70	90		70	90		dB
			Full range	70			70			
k_{SVS}	Supply voltage sensitivity ($\Delta V_{IO}/\Delta V_{CC}$)	$V_{CC} = \pm9$ V to ±15 V	25°C		30	150		30	150	μV/V
			Full range			150			150	
I_{OS}	Short-circuit output current		25°C		±25	±40		±25	±40	mA
I_{CC}	Supply current	No load, $V_O = 0$	25°C		1.7	2.8		1.7	2.8	mA
			Full range			3.3			3.3	
P_D	Total power dissipation	No load, $V_O = 0$	25°C		50	85		50	85	mW
			Full range			100			100	

† All characteristics are measured under open-loop conditions with zero common-mode input voltage unless otherwise specified. Full range for the uA741C is 0°C to 70°C, the uA741I is –40°C to 85°C, and the uA741M is –55°C to 125°C.

NOTE 5: This typical value applies only at frequencies above a few hundred hertz because of the effects of drift and thermal feedback.

uA741C, uA741I, uA741M
GENERAL-PURPOSE OPERATIONAL AMPLIFIERS

operating characteristics, $V_{CC}\pm = \pm15$ V, $T_A = 25°C$

PARAMETER		TEST CONDITIONS		uA741C			uA741I, uA741M			UNIT
				MIN	TYP	MAX	MIN	TYP	MAX	
t_r	Rise time	$V_I = 20$ mV,	$R_L = 2$ kΩ,		0.3			0.3		µs
	Overshoot factor	$C_L = 100$ pF,	See Figure 1		5%			5%		
SR	Slew rate at unity gain	$V_I = 10$ V, $C_L = 100$ pF,	$R_L = 2$ kΩ, See Figure 1		0.5			0.5		V/µs

PARAMETER MEASUREMENT INFORMATION

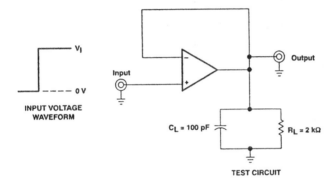

Figure 1. Rise Time, Overshoot, and Slew Rate

APPLICATION INFORMATION

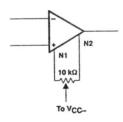

Figure 2. Input Offset Voltage Null Circuit

uA741C, uA741I, uA741M
GENERAL-PURPOSE OPERATIONAL AMPLIFIERS

TYPICAL CHARACTERISTICS

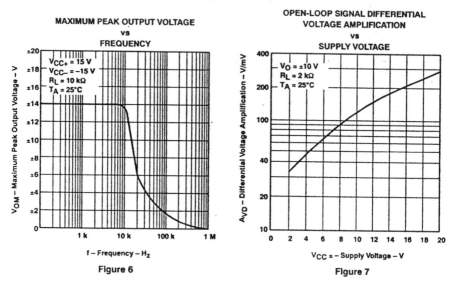

MAXIMUM PEAK OUTPUT VOLTAGE
vs
FREQUENCY

Figure 6

OPEN-LOOP SIGNAL DIFFERENTIAL
VOLTAGE AMPLIFICATION
vs
SUPPLY VOLTAGE

Figure 7

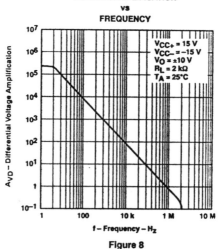

OPEN-LOOP LARGE-SIGNAL DIFFERENTIAL
VOLTAGE AMPLIFICATION
vs
FREQUENCY

Figure 8

TYPICAL CHARACTERISTICS

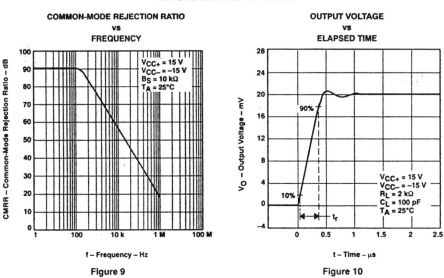

COMMON-MODE REJECTION RATIO
vs
FREQUENCY

Figure 9

OUTPUT VOLTAGE
vs
ELAPSED TIME

Figure 10

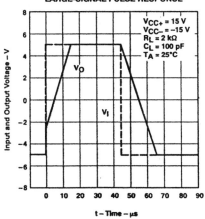

VOLTAGE-FOLLOWER
LARGE-SIGNAL PULSE RESPONSE

Figure 11

High frequency operational amplifier

NE/SE5539

DESCRIPTION
The NE/SE5539 is a very wide bandwidth, high slew rate, monolithic operational amplifier for use in video amplifiers, RF amplifiers, and extremely high slew rate amplifiers.

Emitter-follower inputs provide a true differential input impedance device. Proper external compensation will allow design operation over a wide range of closed-loop gains, both inverting and non-inverting, to meet specific design requirements.

FEATURES
● Bandwidth
  – Unity gain - 350MHz
  – Full power - 48MHz
  – GBW - 1.2GHz at 17dB
● Slew rate: 600/Vμs
● A_{VOL}: 52dB typical
● Low noise - 4nV$\sqrt{}$Hz typical
● MIL-STD processing available

APPLICATIONS
● High speed datacom
● Video monitors & TV
● Satellite communications
● Image processing
● RF instrumentation & oscillators
● Magnetic storage
● Military communications

PIN CONFIGURATION

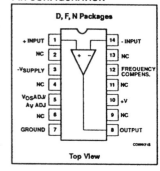

D, F, N Packages

Top View

ORDERING INFORMATION

DESCRIPTION	TEMPERATURE RANGE	ORDER CODE
14-Pin Plastic DIP	0 to +70°C	NE5539N
14-Pin Plastic SO	0 to +70°C	NE5539D
14-Pin Cerdip	0 to +70°C	NE5539F
14-Pin Cerdip	-55 to +125°C	SE5539F

ABSOLUTE MAXIMUM RATINGS[1]

SYMBOL	PARAMETER	RATING	UNITS
V_{CC}	Supply voltage	±12	V
P_{DMAX}	Maximum power dissipation, T_A = 25°C (still-air)[2] F package N package D package	1.17 1.45 0.99	W W W
T_A	Operating temperature range NE SE	0 to 70 -55 to +125	°C °C
T_{STG}	Storage temperature range	-65 to +150	°C
T_J	Max junction temperature	150	°C
T_{SOLD}	Lead soldering temperature (10sec max)	+300	°C

NOTES:
1. Differential input voltage should not exceed 0.25V to prevent excesive input bias current and common-mode voltage 2.5V. These voltage limits may be exceeded if current is limited to less than 10mA.
2. Derate above 25°C, at the following rates:
   F package at 9.3mW/°C
   N package at 11.6mW/°C
   D package at 7.9mW/°C

High frequency operational amplifier **NE/SE5539**

DC ELECTRICAL CHARACTERISTICS

$V_{CC} = \pm8V$, $T_A = 25°C$; unless otherwise specified.

SYMBOL	PARAMETER	TEST CONDITIONS		SE5539			NE5539			UNITS
				MIN	TYP	MAX	MIN	TYP	MAX	
V_{OUT}	Output voltage swing	$R_L = 150\Omega$ to GND and 470Ω to $-V_{CC}$	+Swing				+2.3	+2.7		V
			-Swing				-1.7	-2.2		
V_{OUT}	Output voltage swing	$R_L = 25\Omega$ to GND Over temp	+Swing	+2.3	+3.0					V
			-Swing	-1.5	-2.1					
		$R_L = 25\Omega$ to GND $T_A = 25°C$	+Swing	+2.5	+3.1					V
			-Swing	-2.0	-2.7					
I_{CC+}	Positive supply current	$V_O = 0$, $R_1 = \infty$, Over temp			14	18		2.8	3.5	mA
		$V_O = 0$, $R_1 = \infty$, $T_A = 25°C$			14	17		14	18	mA
I_{CC-}	Negative supply current	$V_O = 0$, $R_1 = \infty$, Over temp			11	15		2.8	3.5	mA
		$V_O = 0$, $R_1 = \infty$, $T_A = 25°C$			11	14		11	15	mA
PSRR	Power supply rejection ratio	$\Delta V_{CC} = \pm1V$, Over temp			300	1000				µV/V
		$\Delta V_{CC} = \pm1V$, $T_A = 25°C$						200	1000	µV/V
A_{VOL}	Large signal voltage gain	$V_O = +2.3V$, $-1.7V$, $R_L = 150\Omega$ to GND, 470Ω to $-V_{CC}$					47	52	57	dB
A_{VOL}	Large signal voltage gain	$V_O = +2.3V$, $-1.7V$	Over temp							dB
		$R_L = 2\Omega$ to GND	$T_A = 25°C$				47	52	57	
A_{VOL}	Large signal voltage gain	$V_O = +2.5V$, $-2.0V$	Over temp	46		60				dB
		$R_L = 2\Omega$ to GND	$T_A = 25°C$	48	53	58				

DC ELECTRICAL CHARACTERISTICS

$V_{CC} = \pm6V$, $T_A = 25°C$; unless otherwise specified.

SYMBOL	PARAMETER	TEST CONDITIONS			SE5539			UNITS
					MIN	TYP	MAX	
V_{OS}	Input offset voltage		Over temp			2	5	mV
			$T_A = 25°C$			2	3	
I_{OS}	Input offset current		Over temp			0.1	3	µA
			$T_A = 25°C$			0.1	1	
I_B	Input bias current		Over temp			5	20	µA
			$T_A = 25°C$			4	10	
CMRR	Common-mode rejection ratio	$V_{CM} = \pm1.3V$, $R_S = 100\Omega$			70	85		dB
I_{CC+}	Positive supply current		Over temp			11	14	mA
			$T_A = 25°C$			11	13	
I_{CC-}	Negative supply current		Over temp			8	11	mA
			$T_A = 25°C$	CmA		8	10	
PSRR	Power supply rejection ratio	$\Delta V_{CC} = \pm1V$	Over temp			300	1000	µV/V
			$T_A = 25°C$					
V_{OUT}	Output voltage swing	$R_L = 150\Omega$ to GND and 390Ω to $-V_{CC}$	Over temp	+Swing		+1.4	+2.0	V
				-Swing		-1.1	-1.7	
			$T_A = 25°C$	+Swing		+1.5	+2.0	
				-Swing		-1.4	-1.8	

High frequency operational amplifier   NE/SE5539

AC ELECTRICAL CHARACTERISTICS

$V_{CC} = \pm8V$, $R_L = 150\Omega$ to GND and 470Ω to $-V_{CC}$, unless otherwise specified.

SYMBOL	PARAMETER	TEST CONDITIONS	SE5539			NE5539			UNITS
			MIN	TYP	MAX	MIN	TYP	MAX	
BW	Gain bandwidth product	$A_{CL} = 7$, $V_O = 0.1\ V_{P-P}$		1200			1200		MHz
	Small signal bandwidth	$A_{CL} = 2$, $R_L = 150\Omega^1$		110			110		MHz
t_S	Settling time	$A_{CL} = 2$, $R_L = 150\Omega^1$		15			15		ns
SR	Slew rate	$A_{CL} = 2$, $R_L = 150\Omega^1$		600			600		V/μs
t_{PD}	Propagation delay	$A_{CL} = 2$, $R_L = 150\Omega^1$		7			7		ns
	Full power response	$A_{CL} = 2$, $R_L = 150\Omega^1$		48			48		MHz
	Full power response	$A_V = 7$, $R_L = 150\Omega^1$		20			20		MHz
	Input noise voltage	$R_S = 50\Omega$, 1MHz		4			4		nV/$\sqrt{Hz}$
	Input noise current	1MHz		6			6		pA/$\sqrt{Hz}$

NOTES:
1. External compensation.

AC ELECTRICAL CHARACTERISTICS

$V_{CC} = \pm6V$, $R_L = 150\Omega$ to GND and 390Ω to $-V_{CC}$, unless otherwise specified.

SYMBOL	PARAMETER	TEST CONDITIONS	SE5539			UNITS
			MIN	TYP	MAX	
BW	Gain bandwidth product	$A_{CL} = 7$		700		MHz
	Small signal bandwidth	$A_{CL} = 2^1$		120		MHz
t_S	Settling time	$A_{CL} = 2^1$		23		ns
SR	Slew rate	$A_{CL} = 2^1$		330		V/μs
t_{PD}	Propagation delay	$A_{CL} = 2^1$		4.5		ns
	Full power response	$A_{CL} = 2^1$		20		MHz

NOTES:
1. External compensation.

TYPICAL PERFORMANCE CURVES

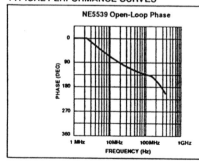

NE5539 Open-Loop Phase

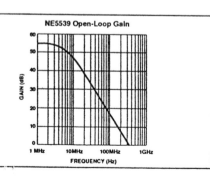

NE5539 Open-Loop Gain

High frequency operational amplifier

NE/SE5539

TYPICAL PERFORMANCE CURVES (Continued)

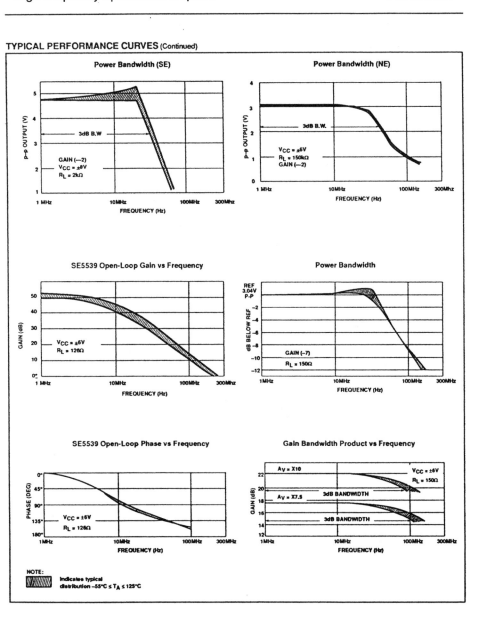

NOTE: Indicates typical distribution $-55°C \leq T_A \leq 125°C$

TLE2027, TLE2027A
EXCALIBUR LOW-NOISE HIGH-SPEED
PRECISION OPERATIONAL AMPLIFIERS
D3440, MAY 1990 – REVISED APRIL 1991

available features

- Outstanding Combination of DC Precision and AC Performance:

  Unity-Gain Bandwidth ... 15 MHz Typ

  V_n... 3.3 nV/$\sqrt{\text{Hz}}$ at f = 10 Hz Typ,
  2.5 nV/$\sqrt{\text{Hz}}$ at f = 1 kHz Typ

  V_{IO} ... 25 µV Max

  A_{VD}... 45 V/µV Typ, With R_L = 2 kΩ,
  19 V/µV Typ, With R_L = 600 Ω

- Available in Standard-Pinout Small-Outline Package

- Output Features Saturation Recovery Circuitry

- Macromodels and Statistical Information

description

The TLE2027 and TLE2027A contain innovative circuit design expertise and high-quality process control techniques to produce a level of ac performance and dc precision previously unavailable in single operational amplifiers. Manufactured using Texas Instruments state-of-the-art Excalibur process, these devices allow upgrades to systems that use lower-precision devices.

In the area of dc precision, the TLE2027 and TLE2027A offer maximum offset voltages of 100 µV and 25 µV, respectively, common-mode rejection ratio of 131 dB (typ), supply voltage rejection ratio of 144 dB (typ), and dc gain of 45 V/µV (typ).

Ac performance is highlighted by a typical unity-gain bandwidth specification of 15 MHz, 55° of phase margin, and noise voltage specifications of 3.3 nV/$\sqrt{\text{Hz}}$ and 2.5 nV/$\sqrt{\text{Hz}}$ at frequencies of 10 Hz and 1 kHz, respectively.

LARGE-SIGNAL
DIFFERENTIAL VOLTAGE AMPLIFICATION
vs
FREQUENCY

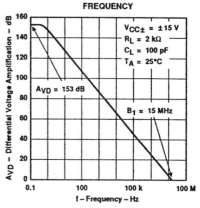

Both the TLE2027 and TLE2027A are available in a wide variety of packages, including the industry-standard 8-pin small-outline version for high-density system applications. The C-suffix devices are characterized for operation from 0°C to 70°C. The I-suffix devices are characterized for operation from –40°C to 105°C. The M-suffix devices are characterized for operation over the full military temperature range of –55°C to 125°C.

AVAILABLE OPTIONS

T_A	V_{IO} max AT 25°C	PACKAGE				
		SMALL-OUTLINE (D)	CHIP CARRIER (FK)	CERAMIC DIP (JG)	METAL CAN (L)	PLASTIC DIP (P)
0°C to 70°C	25 µV	TLE2027ACD	—	—	—	TLE2027ACP
	100 µV	TLE2027CD	—	—	—	TLE2027CP
– 40°C to 105°C	25 µV	TLE2027AID	—	—	—	TLE2027AIP
	100 µV	TLE2027ID	—	—	—	TLE2027IP
– 55°C to 125°C	25 µV	TLE2027AMD	TLE2027AMFK	TLE2027AMJG	TLE2027AML	TLE2027AMP
	100 µV	TLE2027MD	TLE2027MFK	TLE2027MJG	TLE2027ML	TLE2027MP

D packages are available taped and reeled. Add "R" suffix to device type, (e.g., TLE2027ACDR).

TLE2027, TLE2027A
EXCALIBUR LOW-NOISE HIGH-SPEED
PRECISION OPERATIONAL AMPLIFIERS

absolute maximum ratings over operating free-air temperature range (unless otherwise noted)

Supply voltage, V_{CC+} (see Note 1)	22 V
Supply voltage, V_{CC-}	−22 V
Differential input voltage (see Note 2)	±1.2 V
Input voltage range, V_I (any input)	$V_{CC\pm}$
Input current, I_I (each input)	±1 mA
Output current, I_O	±50 mA
Total current into V_{CC+} terminal	50 mA
Total current out of V_{CC-} terminal	50 mA
Duration of short-circuit current at (or below) 25°C (see Note 3)	unlimited
Continuous total dissipation	See Dissipation Rating Table
Operating free-air temperature range, T_A: C-suffix	0°C to 70°C
I-suffix	−40°C to 105°C
M-suffix	−55°C to 125°C
Storage temperature range	−65°C to 150°C
Case temperature for 60 seconds: FK package	260°C
Lead temperature 1,6 mm (1/16 inch) from case for 10 seconds: D or P package	260°C
Lead temperature 1,6 mm (1/16 inch) from case for 60 seconds: JG or L package	300°C

NOTES: 1. All voltage values, except differential voltages, are with respect to the midpoint between V_{CC+} and V_{CC-}.
2. Differential voltages are at the noninverting input with respect to the inverting input. Excessive current will flow if a differential input voltage in excess of approximately ±1.2 V is applied between the inputs unless some limiting resistance is used.
3. The output may be shorted to either supply. Temperature and/or supply voltages must be limited to ensure that the maximum dissipation rating is not exceeded.

DISSIPATION RATING TABLE

PACKAGE	$T_A \leq 25°C$ POWER RATING	DERATING FACTOR ABOVE $T_A = 25°C$	$T_A = 70°C$ POWER RATING	$T_A = 105°C$ POWER RATING	$T_A = 125°C$ POWER RATING
D	725 mW	5.8 mW/°C	464 mW	261 mW	145 mW
FK	1375 mW	11.0 mW/°C	880 mW	495 mW	275 mW
JG	1050 mW	8.4 mW/°C	672 mW	378 mW	210 mW
L	650 mW	5.2 mW/°C	416 mW	234 mW	130 mW
P	1000 mW	8.0 mW/°C	640 mW	360 mW	200 mW

recommended operating conditions

		C-SUFFIX		I-SUFFIX		M-SUFFIX		UNIT
		MIN	MAX	MIN	MAX	MIN	MAX	
Supply voltage, $V_{CC\pm}$		±4	±22	±4	±22	±4	±22	V
Common-mode input voltage, V_{IC}	$T_A = 25°C$	−11	11	−11	11	−11	11	V
	T_A = Full range	−10.5	10.5	−10.4	10.4	−10.2	10.2	
Operating free-air temperature, T_A		0	70	−40	105	−55	125	°C

TLE2027C, TLE2027AC
EXCALIBUR LOW-NOISE HIGH-SPEED
PRECISION OPERATIONAL AMPLIFIERS

electrical characteristics at specified free-air temperature, $V_{CC\pm} = \pm 15$ V (unless otherwise noted)

PARAMETER		TEST CONDITIONS	T_A†	TLE2027C MIN	TYP	MAX	TLE2027AC MIN	TYP	MAX	UNIT
V_{IO}	Input offset voltage		25°C		20	100		10	25	µV
			Full range			145			70	
α_{VIO}	Temperature coefficient of input offset voltage		Full range		0.4	1		0.2	1	µV/°C
	Input offset voltage long-term drift (see Note 4)	$V_{IC} = 0$, $R_S = 50\,\Omega$	25°C		0.006	1		0.006	1	µV/mo
I_{IO}	Input offset current		25°C		6	90		6	90	nA
			Full range			150			150	
I_{IB}	Input bias current		25°C		15	90		15	90	nA
			Full range			150			150	
V_{ICR}	Common-mode input voltage range	$R_S = 50\,\Omega$	25°C	−11 to 11	−13 to 13		−11 to 11	−13 to 13		V
			Full range	−10.5 to 10.5			−10.5 to 10.5			
V_{OM+}	Maximum positive peak output voltage swing	$R_L = 600\,\Omega$	25°C	10.5			10.5			V
			Full range	10			10			
		$R_L = 2\,k\Omega$	25°C	12			12			
			Full range	11			11			
V_{OM-}	Maximum negative peak output voltage swing	$R_L = 600\,\Omega$	25°C	−10.5	−13		−10.5	−13		V
			Full range	−10			−10			
		$R_L = 2\,k\Omega$	25°C	−12	−13.5		−12	−13.5		
			Full range	−11			−11			
A_{VD}	Large-signal differential voltage amplification	$V_O = \pm 11$ V, $R_L = 2\,k\Omega$	25°C	5	45		10	45		V/µV
		$V_O = \pm 10$ V, $R_L = 2\,k\Omega$	Full range	2			4			
		$V_O = \pm 10$ V, $R_L = 1\,k\Omega$	25°C	3.5	38		8	38		
			Full range	1			2.5			
		$V_O = \pm 10$ V, $R_L = 600\,\Omega$	25°C	2	19		5	19		
			Full range	0.5			2			
c_i	Input capacitance		25°C		8			8		pF
z_o	Open-loop output impedance	$I_O = 0$	25°C		50			50		Ω
CMRR	Common-mode rejection ratio	$V_{IC} = V_{ICR}$ min, $R_S = 50\,\Omega$	25°C	100	131		117	131		dB
			Full range	98			114			
k_{SVR}	Supply-voltage rejection ratio ($\Delta V_{CC\pm} / \Delta V_{IO}$)	$V_{CC\pm} = \pm 4$ V to ± 18 V, $R_S = 50\,\Omega$	25°C	94	144		110	144		dB
		$V_{CC\pm} = \pm 4$ V to ± 18 V, $R_S = 50\,\Omega$	Full range	92			106			
I_{CC}	Supply current	$V_O = 0$, No Load	25°C		3.8	5.3		3.8	4.7	mA
			Full range			5.6			4.8	

†Full range is 0°C to 70°C.

NOTE 4: Typical values are based on the input offset voltage shift observed through 168 hours of operating life test at T_A = 150°C extrapolated to T_A = 25°C using the Arrhenius equation and assuming an activation energy of 0.96 eV.

TLE2027C, TLE2027AC
EXCALIBUR LOW-NOISE HIGH-SPEED
PRECISION OPERATIONAL AMPLIFIERS

operating characteristics at specified free-air temperature, $V_{CC\pm} = \pm 15$ V

	PARAMETER	TEST CONDITIONS	$T_A^\dagger$	TLE2027C MIN	TLE2027C TYP	TLE2027C MAX	TLE2027AC MIN	TLE2027AC TYP	TLE2027AC MAX	UNIT
SR	Slew rate at unity gain	$R_L = 2$ kΩ, $C_L = 100$ pF, See Figure 1	25°C	1.7	2.8		1.7	2.8		V/μs
			Full range	1.2			1.2			
V_n	Equivalent input noise voltage (see Figure 2)	$R_S = 100$ Ω, f = 10 Hz	25°C		3.3	8		3.3	4.5	nV/$\sqrt{Hz}$
		$R_S = 100$ Ω, f = 1 kHz			2.5	4.5		2.5	3.8	
$V_{N(PP)}$	Peak-to-peak equivalent input noise voltage	f = 0.1 Hz to 10 Hz	25°C		50	250		50	130	nV
I_n	Equivalent input noise current	f = 10 Hz	25°C		1.5	4		1.5	4	pA/$\sqrt{Hz}$
		f = 1 kHz			0.4	0.6		0.4	0.6	
THD	Total harmonic distortion	$V_O = \pm 10$ V, $A_{VD} = 1$, See Note 5	25°C		< 0.002%			< 0.002%		
B_1	Unity-gain bandwidth (see Figure 3)	$R_L = 2$ kΩ, $C_L = 100$ pF	25°C	7	13		9	13		MHz
B_{OM}	Maximum output-swing bandwidth	$R_L = 2$ kΩ	25°C		30			30		kHz
ϕ_m	Phase margin at unity gain (see Figure 3)	$R_L = 2$ kΩ, $C_L = 100$ pF	25°C		55°			55°		

$\dagger$Full range is 0°C to 70°C.

NOTE 5: Measured distortion of the source used in the analysis was 0.002%.

Low power dual voltage comparator   LM193/A/293/A/393/A/2903

DESCRIPTION

The LM193 series consists of two independent precision voltage comparators with an offset voltage specification as low as 2.0mV max. for two comparators which were designed specifically to operate from a single power supply over a wide range of voltages. Operation from split power supplies is also possible and the low power supply current drain is independent of the magnitude of the power supply voltage. These comparators also have a unique characteristic in that the input common-mode voltage range includes ground, even though operated from a single power supply voltage.

The LM193 series was designed to directly interface with TTL and CMOS. When operated from both plus and minus power supplies, the LM193 series will directly interface with MOS logic where their low power drain is a distinct advantage over standard comparators.

FEATURES

- Wide single supply voltage range 2.0VDC to 36VDC or dual supplies ±1.0VDC, to ±18VDC
- Very low supply current drain (0.8mA) independent of supply voltage (2.0mW/comparator at 5.0VDC)
- Low input biasing current 25nA
- Low input offset current ±5nA and offset voltage ±2mV
- Input common-mode voltage range includes ground
- Differential input voltage range equal to the power supply voltage
- Low output 250mV at 4mA saturation voltage
- Output voltage compatible with TTL, DTL, ECL, MOS and CMOS logic systems

APPLICATIONS

- A/D converters
- Wide range VCO
- MOS clock generator
- High voltage logic gate
- Multivibrators

PIN CONFIGURATION

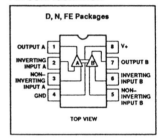

EQUIVALENT CIRCUIT

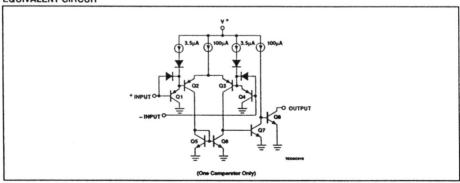

(One Comparator Only)

Low power dual voltage comparator   LM193/A/293/A/393/A/2903

DC AND AC ELECTRICAL CHARACTERISTICS
$+=5VDC$, LM193/193A: $-55°C\ T_A \le +125°C$, unless otherwise specified. LM293/293A: $-25°C\ T_A \le +85°C$, unless otherwise specified.
M393/393A: $0°C\ T_A \le +70°C$, unless otherwise specified. LM2903: $-40°C\ T_A \le +85°C$, unless otherwise specified.

SYMBOL	PARAMETER	TEST CONDITIONS	LM193A			LM293A/393A			LM2903			UNIT
			Min	Typ	Max	Min	Typ	Max	Min	Typ	Max	
V_{OS}	Input offset voltage[2]	$T_A=25°C$		±1.0	±2.0		±1.0	±2.0		±2.0	±7.0	mV
		Over temp.			±4.0			±4.0		±9	±15	mV
V_{CM}	Input common-mode voltage range[3, 6]	$T_A=25°C$	0		V+-1.5	0		V+-1.5	0		V+-1.5	V
		Over temp.	0		V+-2.0	0		V+-2.0	0		V+-2.0	V
V_{IDR}	Differential input voltage[1]	Keep all $V_{INS} \ge 0V_{DC}$ (or V- if need)		V+			V+			V+		V
I_{BIAS}	Input bias current[4]	$I_{IN(+)}$ or $I_{IN(-)}$ with output in linear range $T_A=25°C$		25	100		25	250		25	250	nA
		Over temp.			300			400		200	500	nA
I_{OS}	Input offset current	$I_{IN(+)}-I_{IN(-)}$ $T_A=25°C$		±3.0	±25		±5.0	±50		±5	±50	nA
		Over temp.			±100			±150		±50	±200	nA
I_{OL}	Output sink current	$V_{IN(-)} \ge 1V_{DC}$, $V_{IN(+)}=0$, $V_O \le 1.5V_{DC}$ $T_A=25°C$	6.0	16		6.0	16		6.0	16		mA
I_{OH}	Output leakage current	$V_O=5V_{DC}$, $T_A=25°C$ $V_{IN(+)} \ge 1V_{DC}$, $V_{IN(-)}=0$		0.1			0.1			0.1		μA
		$V_O=30V_{DC}$ Over temp.			1.0			1.0			1.0	nA
I_{CC}	Supply current	$R_L = \infty$ on both comparators.										
		$T_A=25°C$		0.8	1		0.8	1		0.8	1	mA
		V+=30V, over temp.		1	2.5		1	2.5		1	2.5	mA
A_V	Voltage gain	$R_L \ge 15k\Omega$, $V+=15V_{DC}$, $T_A=25°C$	50	200		50	200		25	100		V/mV
V_{OL}	Saturation voltage	$V_{IN(-)} \ge 1V_{DC}$, $V_{IN(+)}=0$, $I_{SINK} \le 4mA$										
		$T_A=25°C$		250	400		250	400		400	400	mV
		Over temp.			700			700			700	mV
t_{LSR}	Large-signal response time	$V_{IN}=$TTL logic swing, $V_{REF}=1.4V_{DC}$, $V_{RL}=5V_{DC}$, $R_L=5.1k\Omega$, $T_A=25°C$		300			300			300		ns
t_R	Response time[5]	$V_{RL}=5V_{DC}$, $R_L=5.1k\Omega$ $T_A=25°C$		1.3			1.3			1.3		μs

Low power dual voltage comparator   LM193/A/293/A/393/A/2903

DC ELECTRICAL CHARACTERISTICS (Continued)

V+=5VDC, LM193/193A: -55°C $T_A \leq$ +125°C, unless otherwise specified. LM293/293A: -25°C $T_A \leq$ +85°C, unless otherwise specified. LM393/393A: 0°C $T_A \leq$ +70°C, unless otherwise specified. LM2903: -40°C $T_A \leq$ +85°C, unless otherwise specified.

SYMBOL	PARAMETER	TEST CONDITIONS	LM193			LM293/393			UNIT
			Min	Typ	Max	Min	Typ	Max	
V_{OS}	Input offset voltage[2]	T_A=25°C		±2.0	±5.0		±2.0	±5.0	mV
		Over temp.			±9.0			±9.0	mV
V_{CM}	Input common-mode voltage range[3,6]	T_A=25°C	0		V±-1.5	0		V+-1.5	V
		Over temp.	0		V±-2.0	0		V+-2.0	V
V_{IDR}	Differential input voltage[1]	Keep all $V_{INS} \geq 0V_{DC}$ (or V-if need)			V+			V+	V
I_{BIAS}	Input bias current[4]	$I_{IN(+)}$ or $I_{IN(-)}$ with output in linear range T_A=25°C		25	100		25	250	nA
		Over temp.			300			400	nA
I_{OS}	Input offset current	$I_{IN(+)}-I_{IN(-)}$ T_A=25°C		±3.0	±25		±5.0	±50	nA
		Over temp.			±100			±150	nA
I_{OL}	Output sink current	$V_{IN(-)} \geq 1V_{DC}$, $V_{IN(+)}$=0, $V_O \leq 1.5V_{DC}$ T_A=25°C	6.0	16		6.0	16		mA
I_{OH}	Output leakage current	$V_{IN(+)} \geq 1V_{DC}$, $V_{IN(-)}$=0, V_O=5VDC T_A=25°C		0.1			0.1		nA
		V_O=30VDC over temp.			1.0			1.0	µA
I_{CC}	Supply current	$R_L=\infty$ on both comparators T_A=25°C		0.8	1		0.8	1	mA
		V+=30V, over temp.			2.5			2.5	mA
A_V	Voltage gain	$R_L \geq 15k\Omega$, V+=15VDC	50	200		50	200		V/mV
V_{OL}	Saturation voltage	$V_{IN(-)} \geq 1V_{DC}$, $V_{IN(+)}$=0, $I_{SINK} \leq 4mA$ T_A=25°C		250	400		250	400	mV
		Over temp.			700			700	mV
t_{LSR}	Large signal response time	V_{IN}=TTL logic swing, V_{REF}=1.4V$_{DC}$, V_{RL}=5V$_{DC}$ R_L=5.1kΩ, T_A=25°C		300			300		ns
t_R	Response time[5]	V_{RL}=5V$_{DC}$, R_L=5.1kΩ T_A=25°C		1.3			1.3		µs

NOTES:

1. Positive excursions of input voltage may exceed the power supply level by 17V. As long as the other voltage remains within the common-mode range, the comparator will provide a proper output state. The low input voltage state must not be less than -0.3V$_{DC}$ (V$_{DC}$ below the magnitude of the negative power supply, if used).
2. At output switch point, $V_O \approx 1.4V_{DC}$, R_S=0Ω with V+ from 5V$_{DC}$ to 30V$_{DC}$ and over the full input common-mode range (0V$_{DC}$ to V+-1.5V$_{DC}$).
3. The input common-mode voltage or either input signal voltage should not be allowed to go negative by more than 0.3V. The upper end of the common-mode voltage range is V+-1.5V, but either or both inputs can go to 30V$_{DC}$ without damage.
4. The direction of the input current is out of the IC due to the PNP input stage. This current is essentially constant, independent of the state of the output so no loading change exists on the reference or input lines.
5. The response time specified is for a 100mV input step with a 5mV overdrive.
6. For input signals that exceed V$_{CC}$, only the overdriven comparator is affected. With a 5V supply, V$_{IN}$ should be limited to 25V maximum, and a limiting resistor should be used on all inputs that might exceed the positive supply.

Low power dual voltage comparator · LM193/A/293/A/393/A/2903

EQUIVALENT CIRCUIT

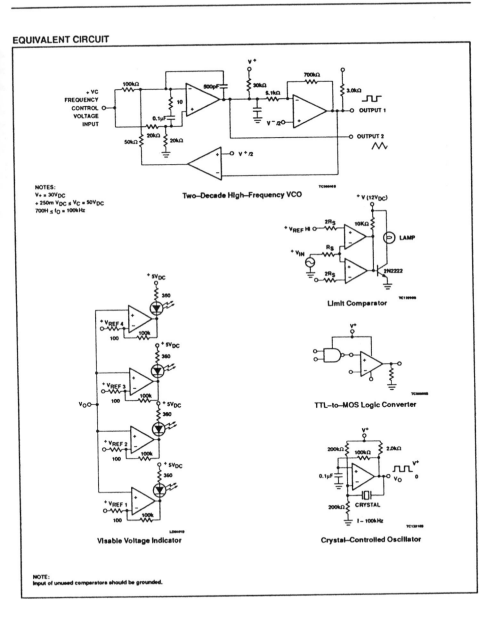

NOTES:
$V_+ = 30V_{DC}$
$+250m\ V_{DC} \le V_C = 50V_{DC}$
$700H \le f_O = 100kHz$

Two–Decade High–Frequency VCO

Limit Comparator

Visable Voltage Indicator

TTL–to–MOS Logic Converter

Crystal–Controlled Oscillator

NOTE:
Input of unused comparators should be grounded.

/VI/IXI/VI

Single/Dual, Ultra-Fast, Low-Power, Precision TTL Comparators

General Description

The MAX913 single and MAX912 dual high-speed, low-power, comparators have differential inputs and complementary TTL outputs. Fast propagation delay (10ns typ), extremely low supply current, and a wide common-mode input range that includes the negative rail make the MAX912/MAX913 ideal for low-power, high-speed, single +5V or ±5V applications such as V/F converters or switching regulators.

The MAX912/MAX913 outputs remain stable through the linear region. This feature eliminates output instability common to high-speed comparators when driven with a slow-moving input signal.

The MAX912/MAX913 can be powered from a single +5V supply or a ±5V split supply. The MAX913 is a pin-for-pin, improved, plug-in replacement for the LT1016. It provides significantly wider input voltage range **and** equivalent speed at a fraction of the power. The MAX912 dual comparator has equal performance to the MAX913 and includes independent Latch controls.

Applications

Zero Crossing Detectors

Ethernet Line Receivers

Switching Regulators

High-Speed Sampling Circuits

High-Speed Triggers

Extended Range V/F Converters

Fast Pulse Width/Height Discriminators

Features

♦ **Ultra Fast (10ns)**

♦ **Single +5V or Dual ±5V Supply Operation**

♦ **Input Range Extends Below Negative Supply**

♦ **Low Power: 7mA (+5V) Per Comparator**

♦ **No Minimum Input Signal Slew Rate Requirement**

♦ **No Power-Supply Current Spiking**

♦ **Stable in the Linear Region**

♦ **Inputs Can Exceed Either Supply**

♦ **Low Offset Voltage: 0.8mV**

Ordering Information

PART	TEMP. RANGE	PIN-PACKAGE
MAX912CPE	0°C to +70°C	16 Plastic DIP
MAX912CSE	0°C to +70°C	16 Narrow SO
MAX912C/D	0°C to +70°C	Dice*
MAX912EPE	-40°C to +85°C	16 Plastic DIP
MAX912ESE	-40°C to +85°C	16 Narrow SO
MAX912MJE	-55°C to +125°C	16 CERDIP
MAX913CPA	0°C to +70°C	8 Plastic DIP
MAX913CSA	0°C to +70°C	8 SO
MAX913C/D	0°C to +70°C	Dice*
MAX913EPA	-40°C to +85°C	8 Plastic DIP
MAX913ESA	-40°C to +85°C	8 SO
MAX913MJA	-55°C to +125°C	8 CERDIP

Dice are specified at T_A = +25°C, DC parameters only.

Pin Configurations

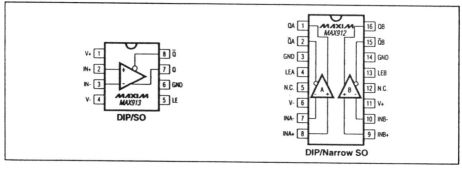

DIP/SO

DIP/Narrow SO

Single/Dual, Ultra-Fast, Low-Power, Precision TTL Comparators

ABSOLUTE MAXIMUM RATINGS

Positive Supply Voltage...7V
Negative Supply Voltage ....-7V
Differential Input Voltage ....±15V
Input Voltage (Referred to V-)..................- 0.3V to 15V
Latch Pin Voltage ....Equal to Supplies
Continuous Output Current...............................±20mA
Continuous Power Dissipation (T$_A$ = +70°C)
  8-Pin Plastic DIP (derate 9.09mW/°C above +70°C) ...727mW
  8-Pin SO (derate 5.88mW/°C above +70°C)...............471mW
  8-Pin CERDIP (derate 8.00mW/°C above +70°C)........640mW

16-Pin Plastic DIP (derate 10.53mW/°C above +70°C)...842mW
16-Pin Narrow SO (derate 8.70mW/°C above +70°C) ...696mW
16-Pin CERDIP (derate 10.00mW/°C above +70°C)....800mW
Operating Temperature Ranges:
  MAX91_ C_ _ ....0°C to +70°C
  MAX91_ E_ _ ....-40°C to +85°C
  MAX91_ MJ_ ....-55°C to +125°C
Storage Temperature Range ....-65°C to +150°C
Lead Temperature (soldering, 10sec) ....+300°C

Stresses beyond those listed under "Absolute Maximum Ratings" may cause permanent damage to the device. These are stress ratings only, and functional operation of the device at these or any other conditions beyond those indicated in the operational sections of the specifications is not implied. Exposure to absolute maximum rating conditions for extended periods may affect device reliability.

ELECTRICAL CHARACTERISTICS

(V+ = +5V, V- = -5V, V$_Q$ = 1.4V, V$_{LE}$ = 0V, T$_A$ = T$_{MIN}$ to T$_{MAX}$, unless otherwise noted.)

PARAMETER	SYMBOL	CONDITIONS			MIN	TYP	MAX	UNITS
Input Offset Voltage (Note 1)	V$_{OS}$	R$_S$ ≤ 100Ω	T$_A$ = +25°C			0.8	2	mV
							3	
Offset Drift	TCV$_{OS}$					2		μV/°C
Input Offset Current (Note 1)	I$_{OS}$		T$_A$ = +25°C			0.3	0.5	μA
							0.8	
Input Bias Current	I$_B$		T$_A$ = +25°C			3	5	μA
		C, E temp. ranges					8	
		M temp. range					10	
Input Voltage Range	V$_{CM}$	C, E temp. ranges			-5.2		+3.5	V
		M temp. range			-5.0		+3.5	
		Single +5V	C, E temp. ranges		-0.2		+3.5	
			M temp. range		0		+3.5	
Common-Mode Rejection Ratio	CMRR	-5.0V ≤ V$_{CM}$ ≤ +3.5V			80	110		dB
Power-Supply Rejection Ratio	PSRR	Positive Supply: 4.5V ≤ V+ ≤ 5.5V			70	85		dB
		Negative Supply: -2V ≥ V- ≥ -7V			80	100		
Small-Signal Voltage Gain	A$_V$	1V ≤ V$_Q$ ≤ 2V, T$_A$ = +25°C			1500	3500		V/V
Output Voltage	V$_{OH}$	V+ ≥ 4.5V	I$_{OUT}$ = 1mA		2.7	3.4		V
			I$_{OUT}$ = 10mA		2.4	3.0		
	V$_{OL}$	I$_{SINK}$ = 4mA				0.3	0.5	
		T$_A$ = +25°C, I$_{SINK}$ = 10mA				0.4		
Positive Supply Current Per Comparator	I+	C, E temp. ranges				7	10	mA
		M temp. range				7	12	
Negative Supply Current Per Comparator	I-					1	2	mA
Latch-Pin High Input Voltage	V$_{IH}$				2.0			V
Latch-Pin Low Input Voltage	V$_{IL}$						0.8	V
Latch-Pin Current	I$_{IL}$	V$_{LE}$ = 0V					-20	μA

Single/Dual, Ultra-Fast, Low-Power, Precision TTL Comparators

ELECTRICAL CHARACTERISTICS (continued)

(V+ = +5V, V- = -5V, V_Q = 1.4V, V_{LE} = 0V, T_A = T_{MIN} to T_{MAX}, unless otherwise noted).

PARAMETER	SYMBOL	CONDITIONS		MIN	TYP	MAX	UNITS
Propagation Delay (Note 2)	t_{PD}	ΔV_{IN} = 100mV, V_{OD} = 5mV	T_A = +25°C		10	14	ns
						16	
		ΔV_{IN} = 100mV, V_{OD} = 20mV	T_A = +25°C		9	12	
						15	
Differential Propagation Delay (Note 2)	Δt_{PD}	ΔV_{IN} = 100mV, V_{OD} = 5mV	T_A = +25°C			3	ns
Channel-to-Channel Propagation Delay (Note 2)		ΔV_{IN} = 100mV, V_{OD} = 5mV (MAX912 only)	T_A = +25°C		500		ps
Latch Setup Time (Note 3)	t_{SU}				2		ns
Latch Hold Time (Note 3)	t_H				2		ns

Note 1: Input Offset Voltage (V_{OS}) is defined as the average of the two input offset voltages, measured by forcing first one output, then the other to 1.4V. Input Offset Current (I_{OS}) is defined the same way.

Note 2: Propagation Delay (t_{PD}) and Differential Propagation Delay (Δt_{PD}) cannot be measured in automatic handling equipment with low input overdrive values. The MAX912/MAX913 are sample tested to 0.1% AQL with a 1V step and 500mV overdrive at +25°C only. Correlation tests show that t_{PD} and Δt_{PD} can be guaranteed with this test, if additional DC tests are performed to guarantee that all internal bias conditions are correct. For low overdrive conditions, V_{OS} is added to the overdrive. Differential Propagation Delay is defined as: t_{PD} = t_{PD} (LH) - t_{PD} (HL)

Note 3: Input latch setup time (t_{SU}) is the interval in which the input signal must be stable prior to asserting the latch signal. The hold time (t_H) is the interval after the latch is asserted in which the input signal must be stable.

Pin Descriptions

PIN MAX913	NAME	FUNCTION
1	V+	Positive power supply. Bypass to GND with a 0.1µF capacitor.
2	IN+	Noninverting input
3	IN-	Inverting input
4	V-	Negative power supply, -5V for dual supply, GND for a single supply
5	LE	Latch enable. Q and $\overline{Q}$ are latched when LE is TTL high or floating. The comparator is transparent when LE is Low.
6	GND	Logic ground
7	Q	TTL output
8	$\overline{Q}$	Complementary TTL output

References

In writing this book I have referred to much previously published material, some of which I recommend to the reader for further reading (marked *). These publications are listed below:

Analog Electronic Circuits; G. M. Glasford; 1986; Prentice Hall *

Digital and Analogue Electronics for HNC; G. C. Loveday; 1993; Longman

Electronic Circuits; D. L. Schilling, C. Belove, T. Apelewicz and R. J. Saccardi; 3rd Edition 1989; McGraw-Hill *

Electronic Noise and Low Noise Design; P. J. Fish; 1993; Macmillan *

Electronics III; D. C. Green; 4th Edition 1988; Longman

Electronics V; D. C. Green; 1993; Longman

Industrial Electronics; N. Morris; McGraw-Hill *

Linear and Interface Circuit Applications; Texas Instruments *

Linear LSI Products Data Book

Operational Amplifiers; G. B. Clayton, B. W. G. Newby; 3rd Edition 1992; Newnes *

Operational Amplifiers and Linear Integrated Circuits; Coughlin & Driscoll; Prentice Hall *

Reference Manual of Transistor Circuits; Mullard Ltd

Work Out Electronics; G. Waterworth; 1988; Macmillan

Index